Get your facts straight with CGP!

This CGP Knowledge Organiser has one mission in life — helping you remember the key facts for Edexcel GCSE Physics.

We've boiled every topic down to the vital definitions, facts and diagrams, making it all easy to memorise.

There's also a matching Knowledge Retriever book that'll test you on every page. Perfect for making sure you know it all!

CGP — still the best! ☺

Our sole aim here at CGP is to produce the highest quality books — carefully written, immaculately presented and dangerously close to being funny.

Then we work our socks off to get them out to you — at the cheapest possible prices.

Contents

Working Scientifically

The Scientific Method....2
Designing & Performing Experiments....3
Presenting Data....4
Conclusions, Evaluations and Units....5

Section 1 — Motion, Forces and Conservation of Energy

Scalars, Vectors and Motion....6
Distance/Time and Velocity/Time Graphs....7
Newton's Laws....8
Weight, Mass and Circular Motion....9
Momentum....10
Reaction Times and Stopping Distances....11
Energy Stores and Transfers....12
Energy Transfers....13
Efficiency and Reducing Energy Loss....14
Energy Resources....15
Energy Resources and Trends in Use....16

Section 2 — Waves and the Electromagnetic Spectrum

Wave Basics....17
Wave Behaviour at Boundaries....18
Sound....19
Ultrasound, Infrasound & Seismic Waves....20
Colour....21
Lenses and Ray Diagrams....22
Ray Diagrams & EM Waves....23
Emitting and Absorbing EM Radiation....24
Uses and Dangers of EM Waves....25

Section 3 — Radioactivity and Astronomy

The Model of the Atom....26
Isotopes and Radioactive Decay....27
Radioactivity....28
Uses of Radiation....29
Nuclear Fission and Fusion....30
The Solar System and Gravity....31
The Universe: Theories & Evidence....32
Stars and Looking into Space....33

Section 4 — Forces and Energy

Work Done, Power and Forces....34
Forces....35
Moments....36

Section 5 — Electricity and Circuits

Current and Circuits....37
Potential Difference & Circuit Symbols....38
Components of Circuits....39
Series and Parallel Circuits....40
Energy and Power in Circuits....41
Electricity at Home....42

Section 6 — Electric and Magnetic Fields

Electric Fields 43
Static Electricity 44
Magnets 45
Compasses and the Motor Effect 46
Motors, Solenoids and Induced P.d. 47
Generators & Electromagnetic Devices 48
Transformers and the National Grid 49

Section 7 — Matter

Density and The Particle Model 50
Heating, Temperature and Pressure 51
Pressure and Work on Gases 52
Elasticity 53
Fluid Pressure and Upthrust 54

Core Practicals

Core Practicals 1 55
Core Practicals 2 56
Core Practicals 3 57
Core Practicals 4 58
Core Practicals 5 59
Core Practicals 6 60

Practical Skills

Apparatus and Techniques 61
Working with Electronics 62

This book only contains the equations that you need to remember.
All other equations will be given to you in the exam.

Published by CGP
From original material by Richard Parsons.

Editors: Josie Gilbert, Sharon Keeley-Holden, Duncan Lindsay, Luke Molloy, Charlotte Sheridan and George Wright.
Contributor: Paddy Gannon.

With thanks to Mark Edwards and Glenn Rogers for the proofreading.
With thanks to Emily Smith for the copyright research.

ISBN: 978 1 78908 847 2

Printed by Elanders Ltd, Newcastle upon Tyne.
Clipart from Corel®
Illustrations by: Sandy Gardner Artist, email sandy@sandygardner.co.uk

The Scientific Method

Developing Theories

Come up with hypothesis
↓
Test hypothesis
↓
Evidence is peer-reviewed
↓
If all evidence backs up hypothesis, it becomes an accepted theory.

HYPOTHESIS — a possible explanation for an observation.

PEER REVIEW — when other scientists check results and explanations before they're published.

Accepted theories can still change over time as more evidence is found, e.g. the theory of atomic structure:

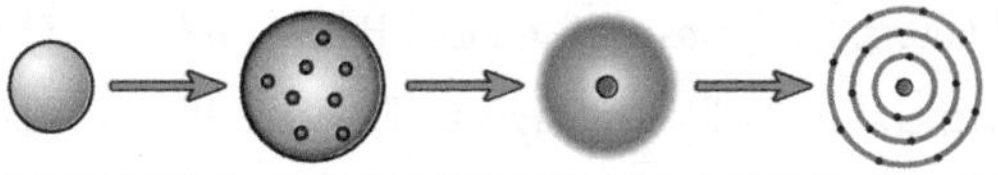

Models

REPRESENTATIONAL MODELS — a simplified description or picture of the real system, e.g. the kinetic theory model of matter:

Models help scientists explain observations and make predictions.

COMPUTATIONAL MODELS — computers are used to simulate complex processes.

Issues in Science

Scientific developments can create four types of issue:

1. **Economic** — e.g. beneficial technology, like alternative energy sources, may be too expensive to use.
2. **Environmental** — e.g. new technology could harm the natural environment.
3. **Social** — decisions based on research can affect society, e.g. taxes on fossil fuels.
4. **Personal** — some decisions affect individuals, e.g. a person may not want a wind farm being built near to their home.

Media reports on scientific developments may be oversimplified, inaccurate or biased.

Hazard and Risk

HAZARD — something that could potentially cause harm.

RISK — the chance that a hazard will cause harm.

Hazards associated with physics experiments include:

Eye damage from lasers.

Faulty electrical equipment.

Fire from Bunsen burners.

The seriousness of the harm and the likelihood of it happening both need consideration.

Designing & Performing Experiments

Collecting Data

Data should be...	
REPEATABLE	Same person gets same results after repeating experiment using the same method and equipment.
REPRODUCIBLE	Similar results can be achieved by someone else, or by using a different method or piece of equipment.
ACCURATE	Results are close to the true answer.
PRECISE	All data is close to the mean.

Reliable data is repeatable and reproducible.

Valid results are repeatable and reproducible and answer the original question.

Fair Tests

INDEPENDENT VARIABLE	Variable that you change.
DEPENDENT VARIABLE	Variable that is measured.
CONTROL VARIABLE	Variable that is kept the same.
CONTROL EXPERIMENT	An experiment kept under the same conditions as the rest of the investigation without anything being done to it.
FAIR TEST	An experiment where only the independent variable changes, whilst all other variables are kept the same.

Controller variables

Control experiments are carried out when variables can't be controlled.

Four Things to Look Out For

1. **RANDOM ERRORS — unpredictable differences caused by things like human errors in measuring.**
2. **SYSTEMATIC ERRORS — measurements that are wrong by the same amount each time.**
3. **ZERO ERRORS — systematic errors that are caused by using a piece of equipment that isn't zeroed properly.**
4. **ANOMALOUS RESULTS — results that don't fit with the rest of the data.**

Anomalous results can be ignored if you know what caused them.

Processing Data

Calculate the mean — add together all repeat measurements and divide by number of measurements.

UNCERTAINTY — the amount by which a mean result may differ from the true value.

$$\text{uncertainty} = \frac{\text{range}}{2}$$

range: largest measurement minus smallest measurement

In any calculation, you should round the answer to the lowest number of significant figures (s.f.) given.

Presenting Data

Bar Charts

Bar charts are used when independent variable is categoric or discrete.

Discrete data can only take certain values with no in-between values.

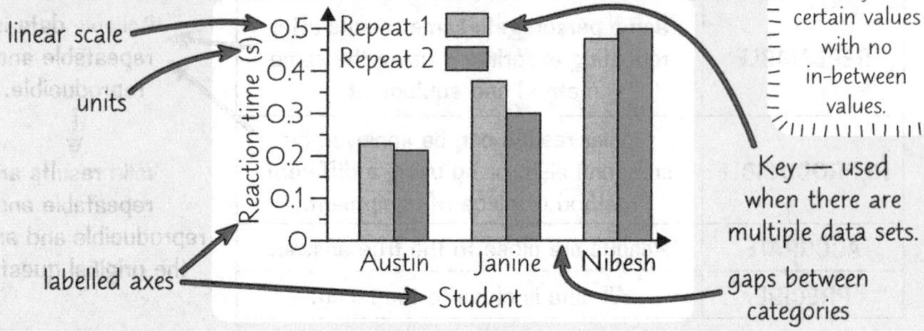

Plotting Graphs

Graphs can be used when both variables are continuous.

Continuous data — can take any numerical value within a range.

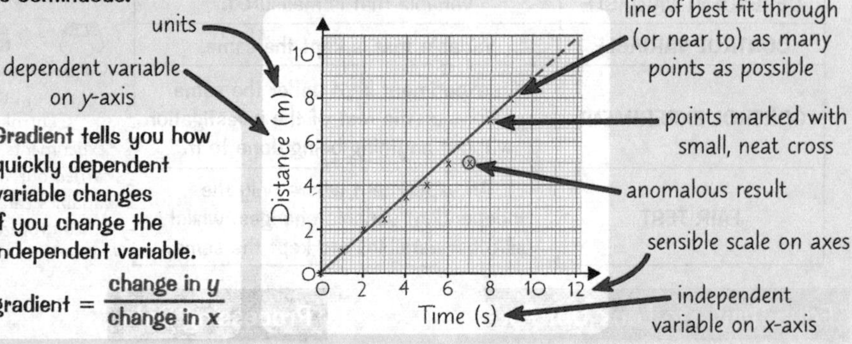
units
dependent variable on y-axis
10
8
6
4
2
0
Distance (m)
0
2
4
6
8
10
12
Time (s)
line of best fit through (or near to) as many points as possible
points marked with small, neat cross
anomalous result
sensible scale on axes
independent variable on x-axis

Gradient tells you how quickly dependent variable changes if you change the independent variable.

$$\text{gradient} = \frac{\text{change in } y}{\text{change in } x}$$

Three Types of Correlation Between Variables

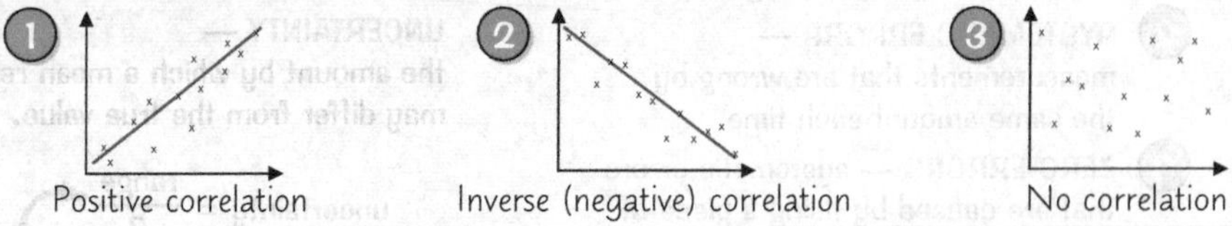

1 Positive correlation

2 Inverse (negative) correlation

3 No correlation

Possible reasons for a correlation:

Chance — **correlation might be a fluke.**

Third variable — **another factor links the two variables.**

Cause — **if every other variable that could affect the result is controlled, you can conclude that changing one variable causes the change in the other.**

Conclusions, Evaluations and Units

Conclusions

Draw conclusion by stating relationship between dependent and independent variables.

↓

Justify conclusion using specific data.

↓

Refer to original hypothesis and state whether data supports it.

You can only draw a conclusion from what your data shows — you can't go any further than that.

Evaluations

EVALUATION — a critical analysis of the whole investigation.

	Things to consider
Method	• Validity of method • Control of variables
Results	• Reliability, accuracy, precision and reproducibility of results • Number of measurements taken • Level of uncertainty in the results
Anomalous results	• Causes of any anomalous results

Repeating experiment with changes to improve the quality of results will give you more confidence in your conclusions.

You could make more predictions based on your conclusion, which you could test in future experiments.

S.I. Units

S.I. BASE UNITS — a set of standard units that all scientists use.

Quantity	S.I. Unit
mass	kilogram (kg)
length	metre (m)
time	second (s)
temperature	kelvin (K)
current	ampere (A)

Scaling Units

SCALING PREFIX — a word or symbol that goes before a unit to indicate a multiplying factor.

Multiple of unit	Prefix
10^{12}	tera (T)
10^{9}	giga (G)
10^{6}	mega (M)
1000	kilo (k)
0.1	deci (d)
0.01	centi (c)
0.001	milli (m)
10^{-6}	micro (μ)
10^{-9}	nano (n)

kg ⇄ g (×1000 / ÷1000)

m^3 ⇄ cm^3 (×10^6 / ÷10^6)

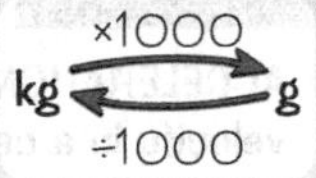

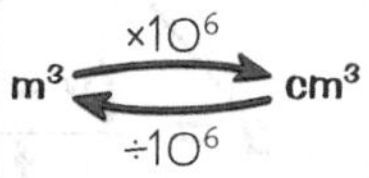

Quantities could be in standard form, e.g. 1×10^2 m = 100 m.

Scalars, Vectors and Motion

Scalars

SCALAR QUANTITIES — only have magnitude and no direction.

- speed
- distance
- mass
- energy

Vectors

VECTOR QUANTITIES — have a magnitude and a direction.

- force
- velocity
- displacement
- acceleration
- momentum
- weight

Distance and Displacement

DISTANCE (scalar) — how far an object has moved (not including its direction).

finish

start

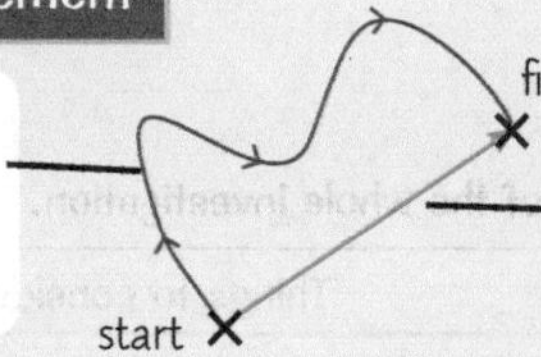

DISPLACEMENT (vector) — the distance and the direction in a straight line from an object's starting point to its finishing point.

Speed and Velocity

 SPEED (scalar) — how fast you're going with no regard to direction.

distance travelled (m) = average speed (m/s) × time (s)

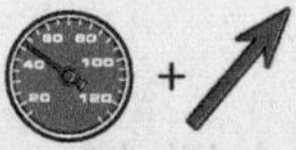

 + VELOCITY (vector) — speed in a certain direction.

Acceleration

ACCELERATION — the change in velocity in a certain amount of time.

acceleration (m/s²)   change in velocity (m/s)

$$a = \frac{(v - u)}{t}$$

(v is final velocity and u is initial velocity)

time (s)

Acceleration of object due to gravity close to Earth's surface (object in free fall) is roughly 10 m/s².

Typical Speeds

		Typical speed (m/s)
	walking	1.4
	running	3
	cycling	5.5
	car (built-up area)	13
	car (motorway)	31
	train	up to 55
	plane	250
	wind	5 - 20
	sound	340

Objects, sound and wind rarely travel at a constant speed.

Distance/Time and Velocity/Time Graphs

Distance/Time Graphs

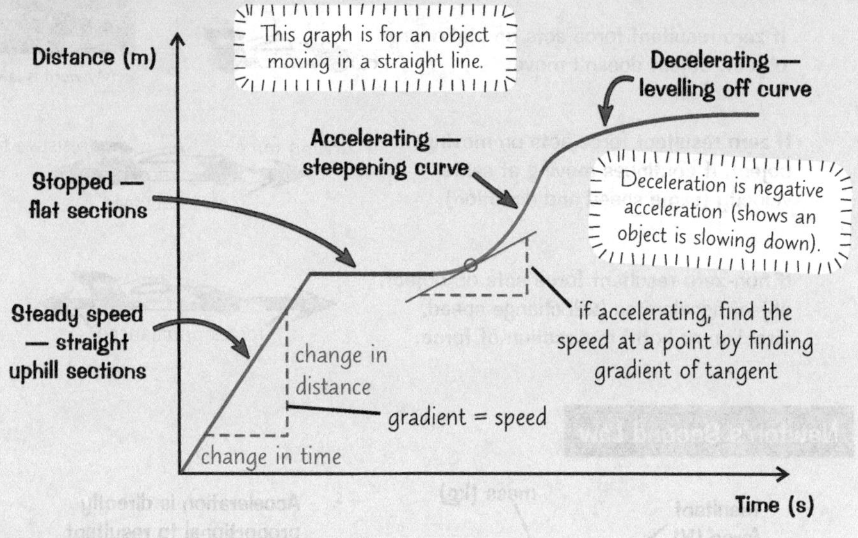

Velocity/Time Graphs

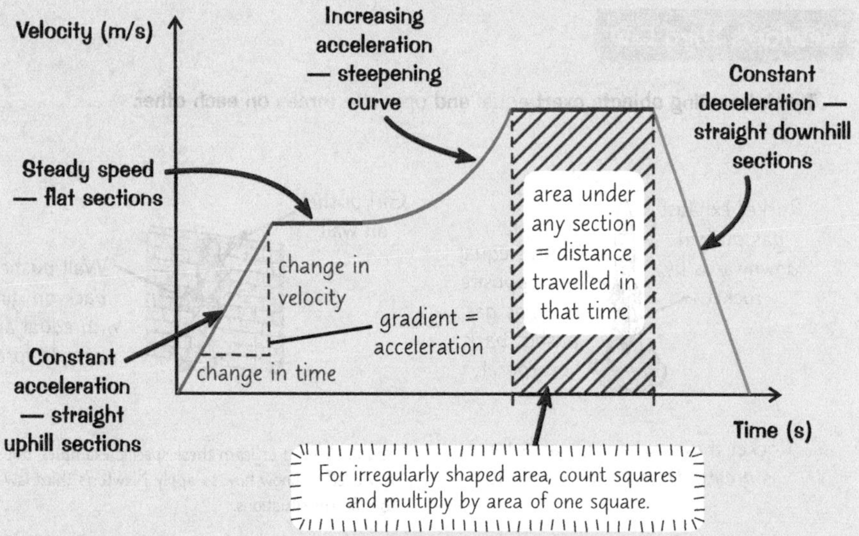

Newton's Laws

Newton's First Law

If zero resultant force acts on stationary object, object doesn't move.

If zero resultant force acts on moving object, it continues moving at same velocity (same speed and direction).

If non-zero resultant force acts on object, object accelerates (will change speed, direction or both) in direction of force.

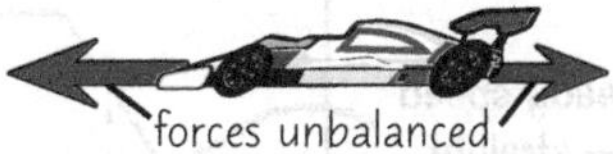

Newton's Second Law

$$F = ma$$

- **resultant force (N)** — F
- **mass (kg)** — m
- **acceleration (m/s²)** — a

- **Acceleration is directly proportional to resultant force — $F \propto a$.**
- **Acceleration is inversely proportional to mass.**

Newton's Third Law

Two interacting objects exert equal and opposite forces on each other.

Rocket moves when upwards force is greater than rocket's weight.

Girl pushes on wall.
Wall pushes back on girl with equal and opposite force.

You don't need to learn these specific examples, but you need to know how to apply Newton's third law to different situations.

Weight, Mass and Circular Motion

Weight, Mass and Gravity

WEIGHT — force that acts on an object due to gravity.

$$W = mg$$

weight (N) — W
mass (kg) — m
gravitational field strength (N/kg) — g

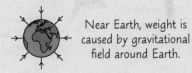

Near Earth, weight is caused by gravitational field around Earth.

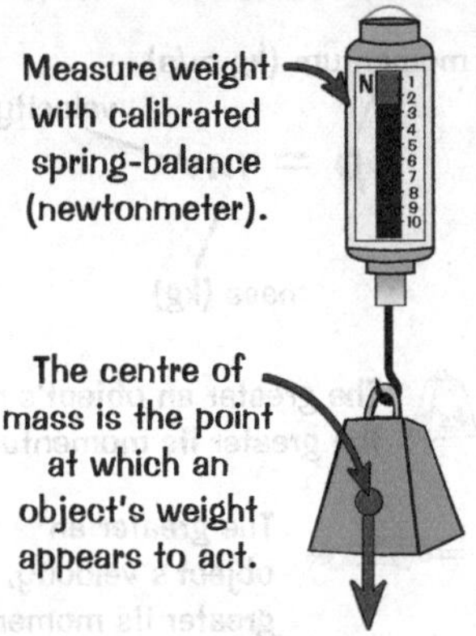

Measure weight with calibrated spring-balance (newtonmeter).
N
1
2
3
4
5
6
7
8
9
10
The centre of mass is the point at which an object's weight appears to act.

- **Object weight depends on strength of gravitational field at object location.**
- **Object mass has same value anywhere in the Universe.**

Mass and Motion

INERTIAL MASS — measure of how hard it is to change an object's velocity. It's the ratio of force over acceleration: $m = F \div a$.

Same force applied to bowling ball and golf ball.

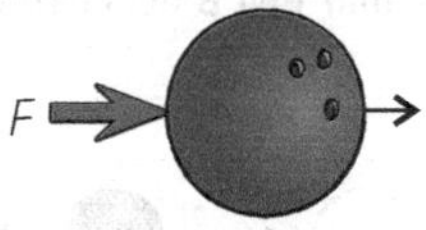

smaller acceleration

bigger acceleration

Bowling ball has bigger inertial mass, so it's harder to increase its velocity.

Circular Motion

Object in circular motion with constant speed is always changing direction, so object has changing velocity.

Changing velocity means object is accelerating, so there is a resultant force on it.

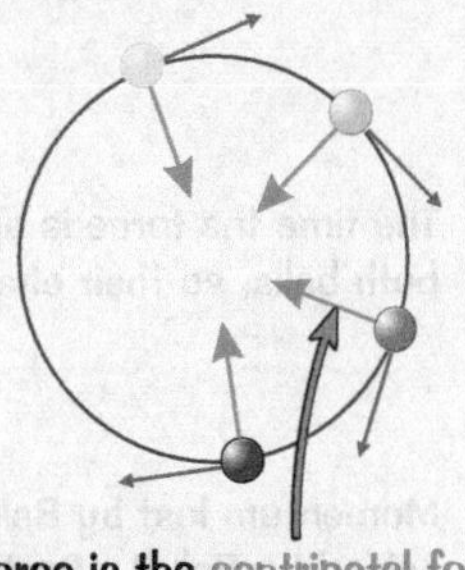

This force is the centripetal force. It always acts towards the centre of the circle.

Momentum

Calculating Momentum

momentum (kg m/s)

$$p = mv$$

velocity (m/s)

mass (kg)

The greater an object's mass, the greater its momentum.

The greater an object's velocity, the greater its momentum.

Conservation of Momentum

CONSERVATION OF MOMENTUM — in a closed system, total momentum before an event (e.g. a collision) equals total momentum after an event.

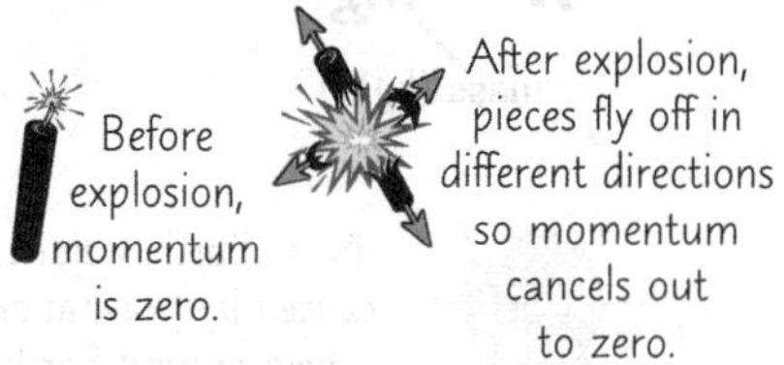

Before explosion, momentum is zero.
After explosion, pieces fly off in different directions so momentum cancels out to zero.

Newton's Third Law and Momentum

For two balls of the same mass:

"Yes, it's definitely revision, I promise..."

Ball A approaches with momentum *p* and collides with Ball B.

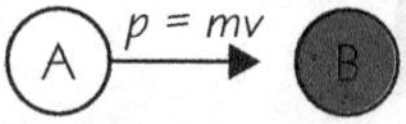

↓

Ball A and Ball B exert equal and opposite forces on each other due to Newton's Third Law.

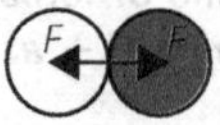

↓

Due to $F = ma$, Ball A decelerates at the same rate that Ball B accelerates.

↓

The time the force is applied is the same for both balls, so their change in speed is the same.

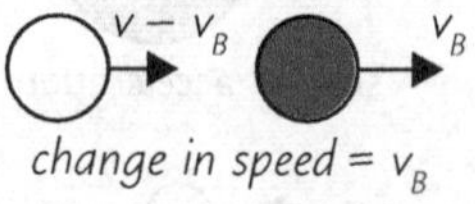

↓

Momentum lost by Ball A equals momentum gained by Ball B. So total momentum before equals total momentum after.

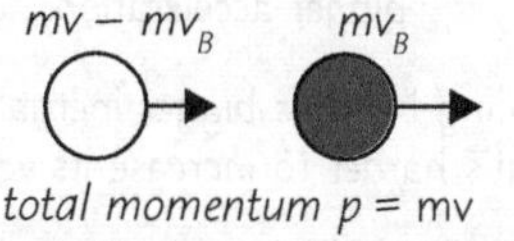

Reaction Times and Stopping Distances

Reaction Times

Typical human reaction time: 0.2 - 0.9 s. Three factors affecting reaction times:

1. Tiredness
2. Drugs and alcohol
3. Distractions

Three Steps to do the Ruler Drop Test

1. Get someone to hold ruler so zero is between your thumb and forefinger.

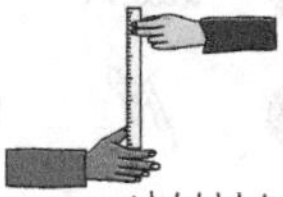

2. Ruler dropped without warning. Catch it as quickly as possible.
3. Use distance ruler fell to calculate reaction time.

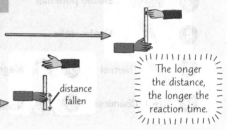

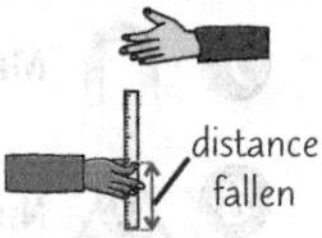

The longer the distance, the longer the reaction time.

Stopping Distance Equation

Stopping distance = Thinking distance + Braking distance

Thinking distance: How far vehicle moves during driver's reaction time.

Braking distance: Distance taken to stop whilst brakes are applied.

Two factors that increase thinking distance:

1. faster vehicle speed
2. long driver reaction times

Four factors that increase braking distance:

1. faster vehicle speed
2. heavier vehicle
3. poor, wet or icy road surface
4. damaged or worn brakes or tyres

If speed doubles, thinking distance doubles and braking distance quadruples.

Work Done When Stopping

For car to stop, work done by brakes equals energy in car's kinetic energy store.

$$\frac{1}{2} \times m \times v^2 = F \times d$$

- m = mass of car (kg)
- v = speed of car (m/s)
- F = braking force (N)
- d = braking distance (m)

A good estimate for a car's mass ~ 1000 kg.

Large Decelerations

The faster a vehicle is going, the greater the braking force needed to make it stop in a certain distance.

↓

Larger braking force means larger deceleration.

Very large deceleration can cause:

brakes to overheat

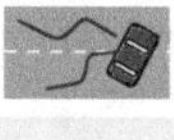
vehicle to skid

Energy Stores and Transfers

Eight Types of Energy Store

 ① Kinetic

② Gravitational potential

③ Elastic potential

④ Electrostatic

⑤ Thermal ⑦ Magnetic

⑥ Chemical ⑧ Nuclear

Four Types of Energy Transfer

① Mechanical (a force doing work)

② Electrical (work done by moving charges)

③ Heating

④ Radiation (e.g. light or sound)

Kinetic Energy

kinetic energy (J)

$$KE = \frac{1}{2}mv^2$$

mass (kg) speed (m/s)

Gravitational Potential Energy

change in gravitational potential energy (J)

mass (kg) change in vertical height (m)

$$\Delta GPE = mg\Delta h$$

gravitational field strength (N/kg)

Systems and Conservation of Energy

SYSTEM — a single object or a group of objects.

CONSERVATION OF ENERGY — energy can be transferred usefully, stored or dissipated but not created or destroyed.

CLOSED SYSTEM — no energy (or matter) is transferred in or out of the system, so there is no net change in total energy.

Clothed system.

Pan and hob = NOT a closed system.
Energy is transferred away to surroundings.

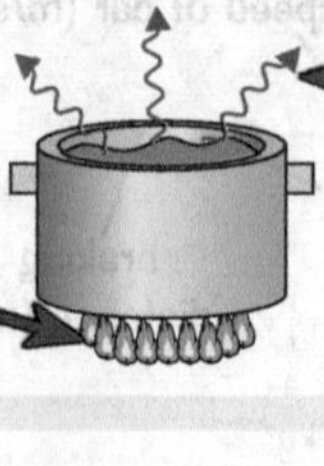

Energy transferred usefully (by heating) to thermal energy store of pan, increasing its temperature.

Some energy dissipated as energy transferred to thermal energy stores of surroundings.

Energy Transfers

Energy Transfer Diagrams for Six Different Systems

1 Arm throwing ball up

Chemical energy store of arm

↓ work done mechanically by force exerted by arm

Kinetic energy store of ball and arm

2 Ball falling

Gravitational potential energy store of ball

↓ work done mechanically by gravitational force

Kinetic energy store of ball

3 Ball rolling up smooth slope

Kinetic energy store of ball

↓ work done mechanically by gravitational force

Gravitational potential energy store of ball

4 Car slowing down without braking

Kinetic energy store of car

↓ work done mechanically by friction and then by heating

Thermal energy stores of car and surroundings

5 Car hitting tree

Kinetic energy store of car

→ work done mechanically by normal contact force → **Various energy stores: e.g. elastic potential energy stores of car and tree, thermal energy stores of car and tree**

→ energy transferred away by sound waves →

6 Kettle boiling water

mains → energy transferred electrically →  **Thermal energy store of kettle's heating element** → energy transferred by heating → **Thermal energy store of water**

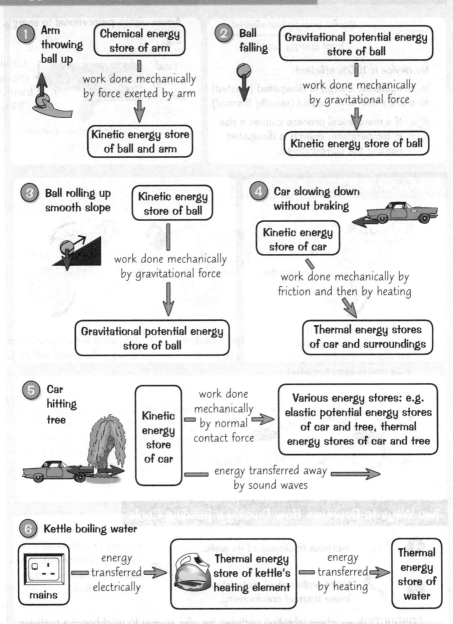

Efficiency and Reducing Energy Loss

Efficiency Equation

$$\text{Efficiency} = \frac{\text{Useful energy transferred}}{\text{Total energy supplied}}$$

No device is 100% efficient.

In all systems, energy is dissipated (wasted) to a store that's not useful (usually thermal).

If a mechanical process causes a rise in temperature, energy is dissipated heating the surroundings.

Efficiency in Diagrams

Arrow widths proportional to energy. E.g.

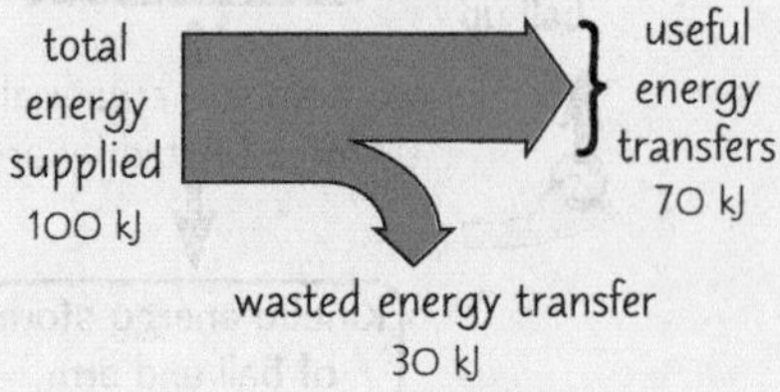

Lubrication and Thermal Insulation

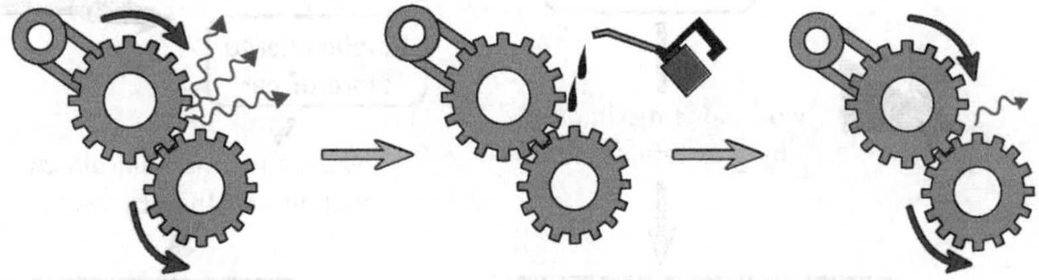

Frictional force acts between moving gears, so energy dissipated (an unwanted energy transfer).

Apply lubricant (e.g. oil).

Frictional force reduced so energy dissipated reduced.

Thermal insulation (e.g. cotton wool) reduces unwanted energy transfers by heating.

Lubrication and thermal insulation increase the efficiency of useful energy transfers.

Two Ways to Decrease How Quickly a Building Cools

1. **Increase thickness of its walls.**
2. **Make walls out of material with lower thermal conductivity.**

The higher a material's thermal conductivity, the faster it transfers energy by conduction.

CONDUCTION — where vibrating particles transfer energy to neighbouring particles.

Energy Resources

Non-Renewable and Renewable Energy Resources

NON-RENEWABLE ENERGY RESOURCES — energy resources that will run out one day.

RENEWABLE ENERGY RESOURCES — energy resources that will never run out.

Three Fossil Fuels

☒ Non-renewable

1 Coal

2 Oil

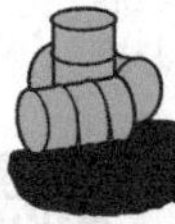

Used to make fuel (petrol and diesel) for cars.

3 (Natural) Gas

Used to heat homes and cook food.

All three fossil fuels are burned to generate electricity.

- **Burning fossil fuels releases CO_2, contributing to global warming.**
- **Burning coal and oil releases sulfur dioxide, causing acid rain.**

Tidal Power

☑ Renewable

Tide comes in.

↓

Water builds behind the dam.

↓

Water allowed out through turbines.

↓

Electricity generated.

Tidal barrage — big dams built across river estuaries.

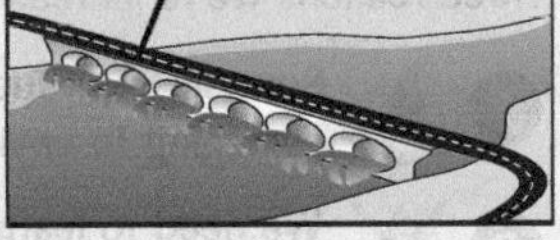

Call that a big dam?

- **Produce no pollution when in use.**
- **Disturb habitats of nearby wildlife and spoil the view.**

Nuclear Power

☒ Non-renewable

Nuclear fuel undergoes fission in nuclear reactors, generating electricity.

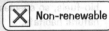

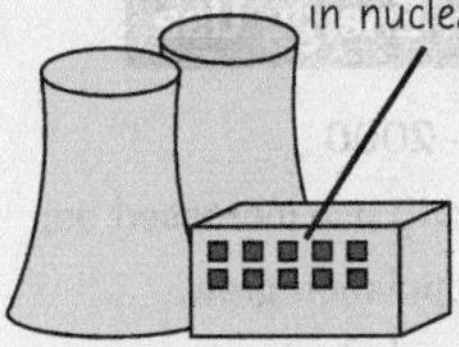

- **Nuclear waste is dangerous and difficult to dispose of.**
- **Carries the risk of a major catastrophe.**

Energy Resources and Trends in Use

Solar Power

☑ Renewable

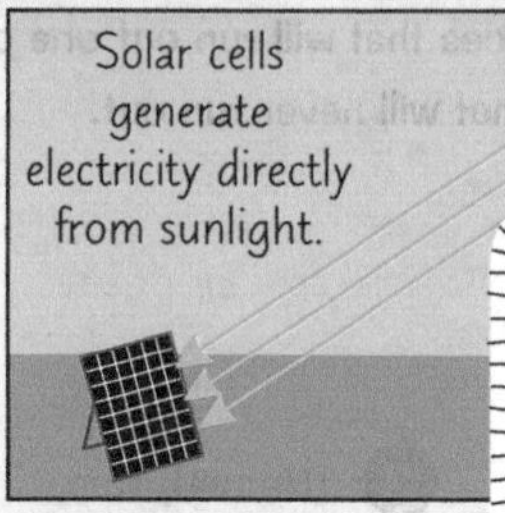
Solar cells generate electricity directly from sunlight.

Solar water heaters use the sun to heat water which is then pumped into radiators.

- **Produce no pollution when in use.**

Wind Power

☑ Renewable

Wind turns wind turbines, generating electricity.

- **Produce no pollution when in use.**
- **Noisy and spoil the view.**

Bio-fuels

☑ Renewable

Made from plant products or animal dung.

Bio-fuels are burned to generate electricity, and used as fuel in some cars.

- **In some regions, large areas of forest destroyed to grow bio-fuels, so species lose natural habitats.**

Hydro-electric Power

☑ Renewable

Big dams built so valley fills up with water.
Water allowed out through turbines, generating electricity.

- **Produce no pollution when in use.**
- **Flooding valley has big impact on environment and can cause loss of animal habitats.**

Trends in Energy Use

1900 – 2000

Electricity use increased as:

- **population grew.**
- **people began to use electricity for more things.**

2000 onwards

Electricity use decreasing as:

- **appliances are more efficient.**
- **people are more careful with amount of energy use.**

Three reasons we're increasing use of renewables:

1. **Burning fossil fuels is very damaging to environment.**
2. **We need to learn how to get by without non-renewables before they run out.**
3. **Pressure on governments and companies has led them to introduce renewable energy targets.**

Changing to renewables is limited by their cost and issues with reliability.

Wave Basics

Wave Properties

When waves travel through a medium, they transfer energy and information (but not matter).

Sound waves move away...

...the air particles don't.

Ripples on water's surface move away...

...the water doesn't.

FREQUENCY — number of complete cycles of the wave passing a certain point each second.

PERIOD — amount of time it takes for one full cycle of a wave.

period = 1 ÷ frequency

AMPLITUDE — maximum displacement of a point on a wave from its rest position.

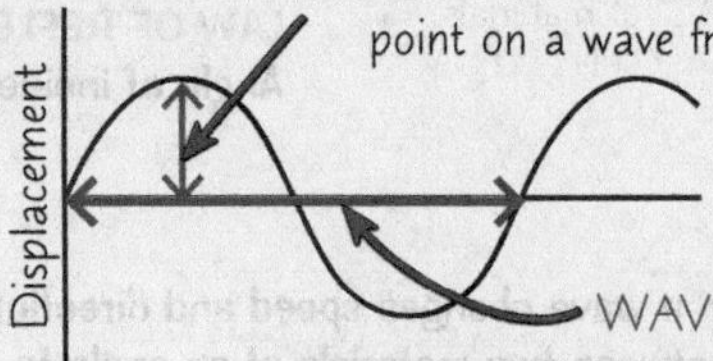

WAVELENGTH — length of a full cycle of a wave.

Transverse Waves

Vibrations perpendicular (at 90°) to direction wave travels.

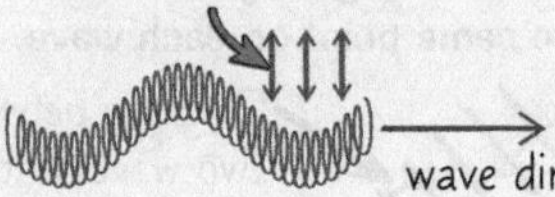

Three types of transverse waves:

1. 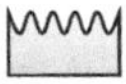 **Ripples in water**
2.  **Electromagnetic waves (e.g. light)**
3.  **S-waves**

Longitudinal Waves

Vibrations parallel to direction wave travels.

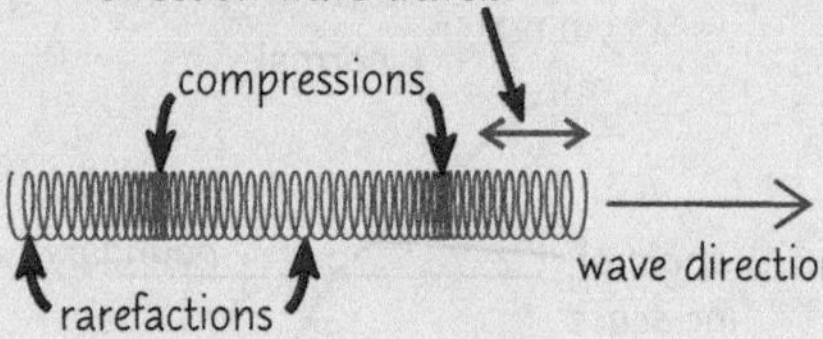

Two types of longitudinal waves:

1.  **Sound waves**
2.  **P-waves**

Wave Speed

WAVE SPEED — how quickly a wave moves through space.

Wave velocity is the wave's speed AND direction.

$$v = \frac{x}{t}$$

wave speed (m/s), distance (m), time (s)

$$v = f\lambda$$

wave speed (m/s), frequency (hertz, Hz), wavelength (m)

Wave Behaviour at Boundaries

Boundaries

When a wave hits a boundary, it can be...

- **absorbed**
- **reflected**
- **or transmitted:**
  - **not refracted**
  - **refracted**

What happens depends on wavelength of wave and properties of materials.

Reflection

The normal is a line perpendicular to surface at point of incidence.

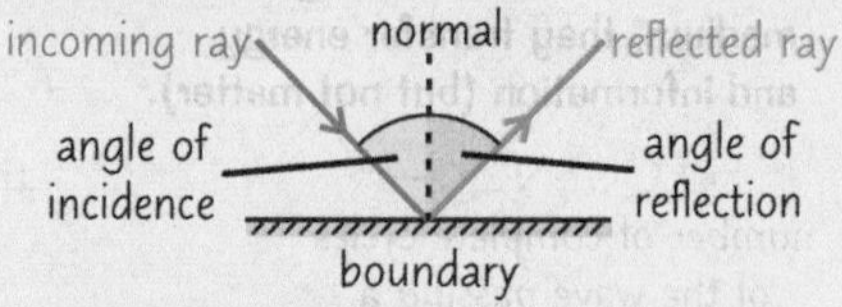

LAW OF REFLECTION — Angle of incidence = angle of reflection.

Refraction

REFRACTION — when a wave changes speed and direction as it crosses a boundary between two materials at an angle to the normal.

Frequency never changes during refraction.

Wave refracts
- **slows down → Wavelength decreases. → Bends towards normal.**
- **speeds up → Wavelength increases. → Bends away from normal.**

Typically, EM waves slow down in denser materials, and speed up in less dense materials.

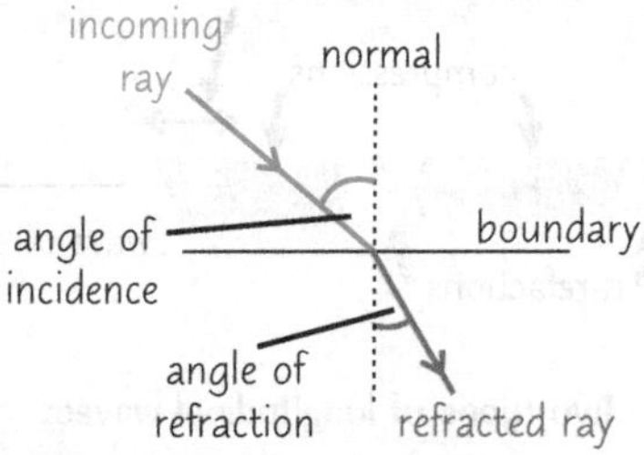

WAVEFRONT — an imaginary line that represents the same point on each wave.

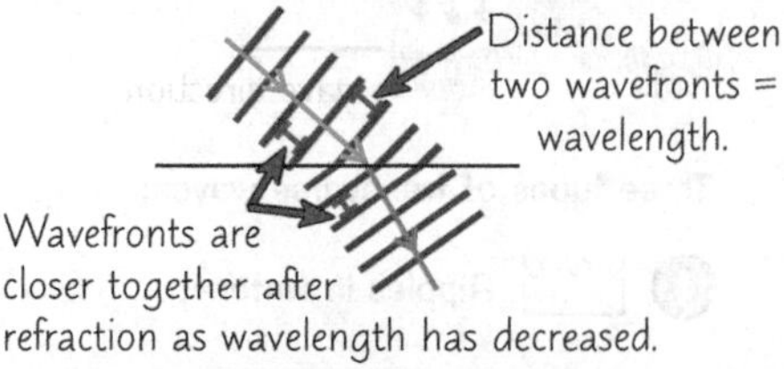

Total Internal Reflection

TOTAL INTERNAL REFLECTION — when all light incident on a boundary is reflected back.

CRITICAL ANGLE — the minimum angle at which total internal reflection occurs.

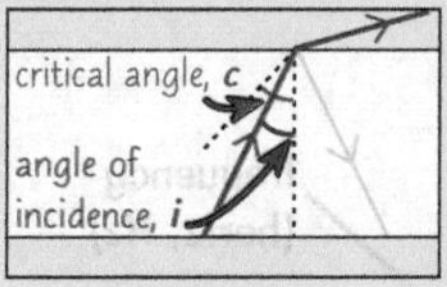

i* < *c

Mostly refracted, some reflected

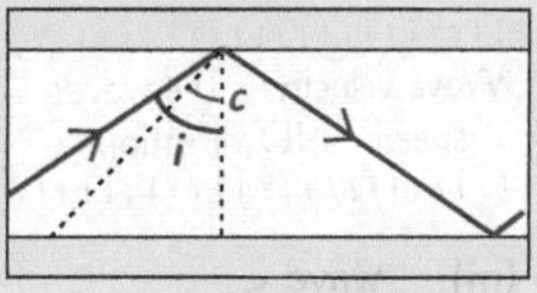

i* > *c

Total internal reflection

Diffuse Reflection

Rays reflected in all directions

Rough surfaces (e.g. paper) appear matt.

Specular Reflection

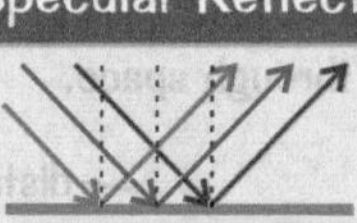

Rays reflected in one direction

Smooth surfaces (e.g. mirrors) give clear reflection.

Sound

Vibrations

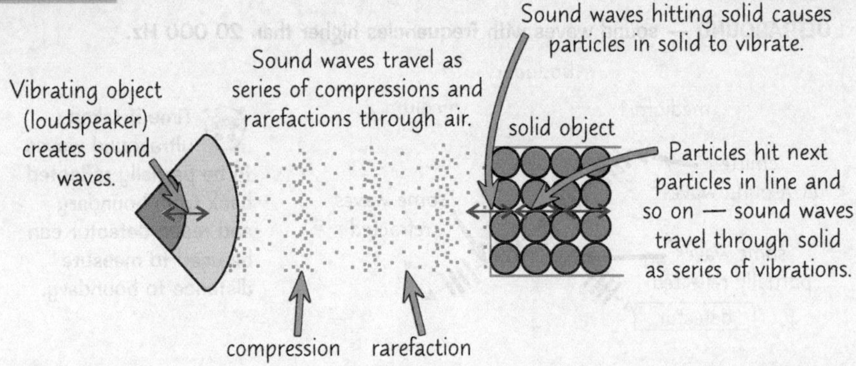
Sound waves hitting solid causes particles in solid to vibrate.
Sound waves travel as series of compressions and rarefactions through air.
Vibrating object (loudspeaker) creates sound waves.
solid object
Particles hit next particles in line and so on — sound waves travel through solid as series of vibrations.
compression
rarefaction

When a wave enters a medium and speeds up:

- **wavelength increases**
- **frequency stays the same**

Hearing Sound

Sound waves reach ear.

↓

Cause eardrum to vibrate.

↓

These vibrations cause other parts of ear to vibrate, allowing you to hear the sound waves.

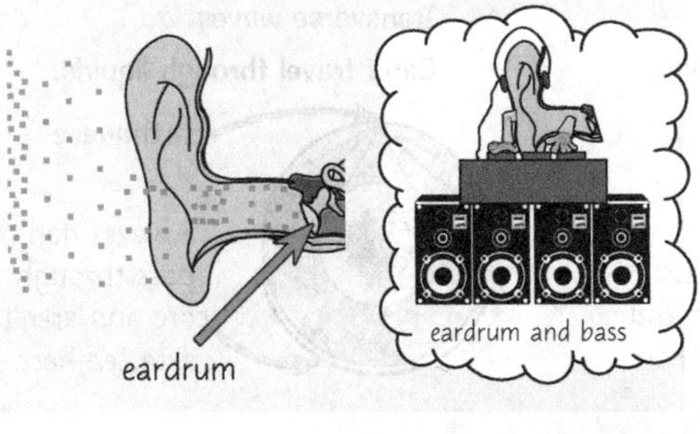
eardrum
eardrum and bass

Limited Frequency Range

Conversion of sound waves to vibrations in a solid object only occurs over a certain frequency range.

Three factors that limit frequency range are the solid object's:

1. **Size.**
2. **Shape.**
3. **Structure.**

E.g. in human hearing, conversion of sound to vibrations is limited by size and shape of eardrum, and structure of vibrating parts.

Ultrasound, Infrasound & Seismic Waves

Ultrasound

ULTRASOUND — sound waves with frequencies higher than 20 000 Hz.

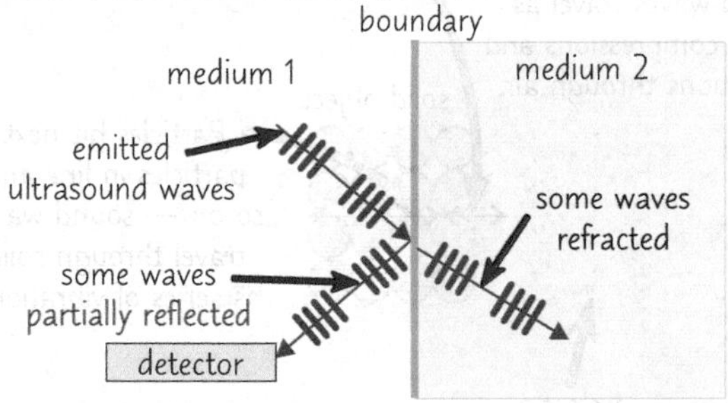

Time it takes ultrasound waves to be partially reflected back from boundary and reach detector can be used to measure distance to boundary.

Two uses of ultrasound:

1.

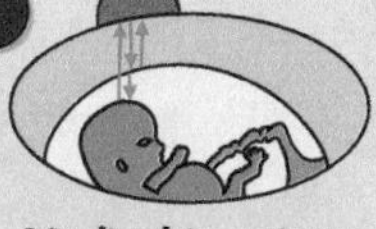

Medical imaging, e.g. pre-natal scanning of foetus.

2.

Echo sounding (sonar), e.g. finding depth of water or locating objects in deep water.

To find distance to sea floor/object, halve the time taken for ultrasound to travel there and back. Use this time along with wave speed in $x = vt$.

Seismic Waves

INFRASOUND — sound waves with frequencies lower than 20 Hz.

Scientists can monitor infrasound to predict natural events e.g. volcanoes.

Earthquakes produce seismic waves at a range of frequencies — including infrasound.
Detecting seismic waves gives evidence for size of Earth's core and Earth's structure:

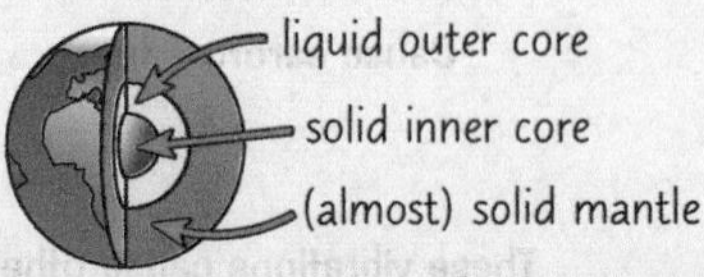

P-waves

- **Longitudinal waves.**
- **Travel through solids and liquids.**

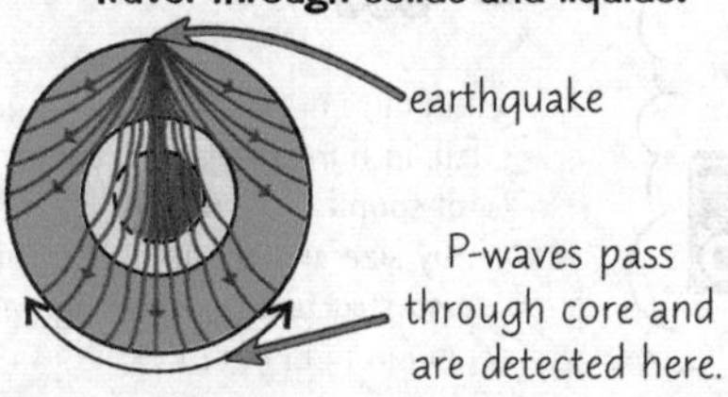

earthquake
P-waves pass through core and are detected here.

S-waves

- **Transverse waves.**
- **Can't travel through liquids.**

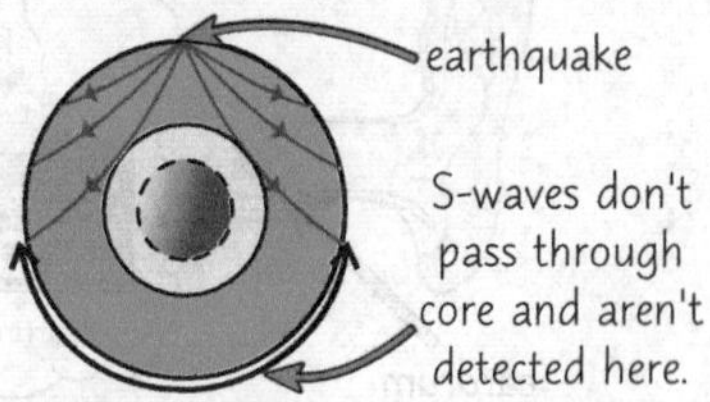

earthquake
S-waves don't pass through core and aren't detected here.

Colour

Colour and Wavelength

In the visible light spectrum, every colour has a small range of wavelengths.

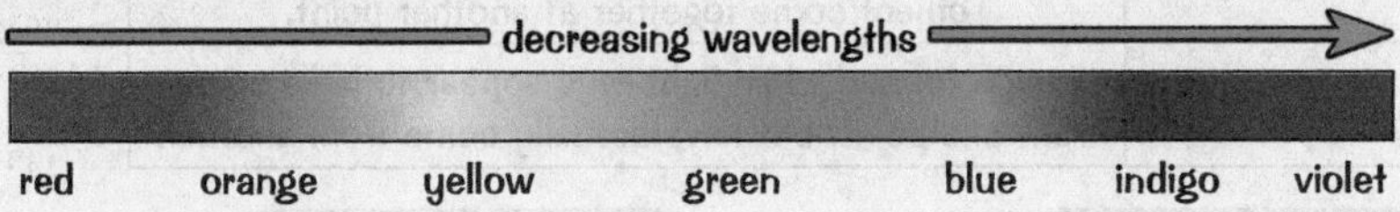
decreasing wavelengths
red
orange
yellow
green
blue
indigo
violet

- **Opaque objects don't transmit light.**
- **Colour depends on wavelengths of light that are most reflected.**

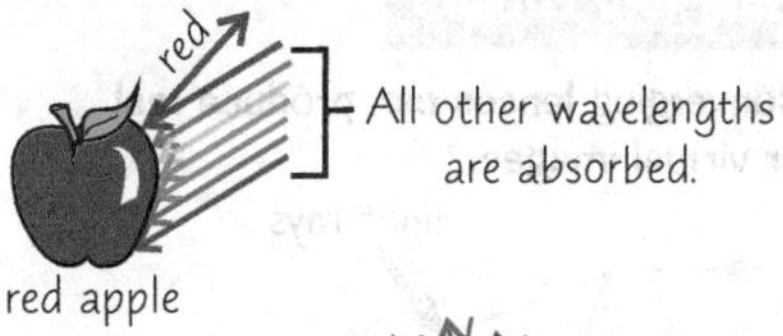
red
All other wavelengths are absorbed.
red apple

Black objects absorb all wavelengths of visible light.

White objects reflect all wavelengths of visible light equally.

- **Transparent (see-through) or translucent (partially see-through) objects transmit light.**
- **Colour depends on wavelengths of light transmitted and reflected.**

white

White light is made up of all colours.

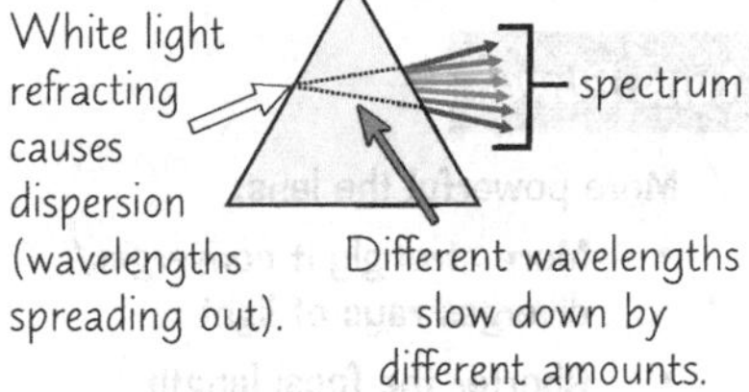
White light refracting causes dispersion (wavelengths spreading out).
spectrum
Different wavelengths slow down by different amounts.

Colour Filters

Colour filters transmit certain colours (wavelengths) and absorb the rest.

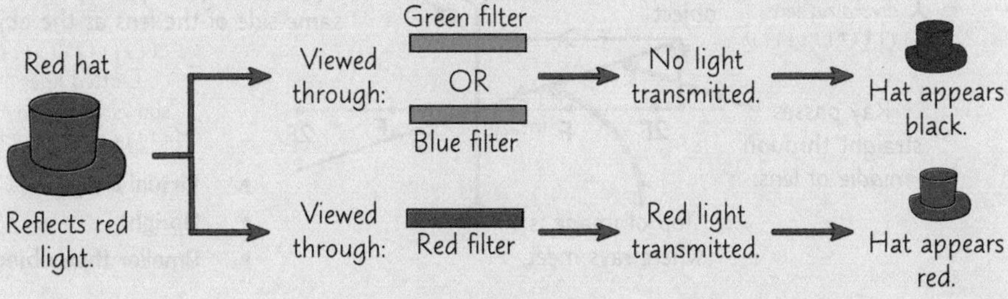
Red hat
Reflects red light.
Viewed through:
Green filter
OR
Blue filter
No light transmitted.
Hat appears black.
Viewed through:
Red filter
Red light transmitted.
Hat appears red.

Lenses and Ray Diagrams

Images

REAL IMAGE	Image formed when light rays from a point on an object come together at another point.
VIRTUAL IMAGE	Image formed when light rays appear to have come from one point, but have actually come from another.

Lenses form images by refracting light.

Converging Lenses

Converging lenses can produce real or virtual images.

light rays

F

axis

Focal length — distance between centre of the lens and principal focus.

Principal focus — point where rays hitting lens parallel to axis come together.

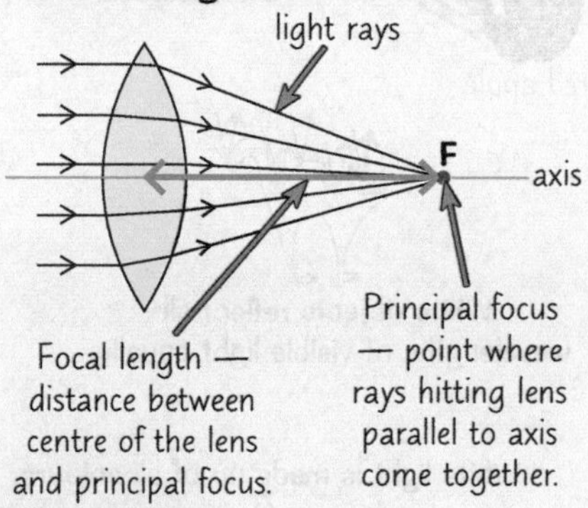

Diverging Lenses

Diverging lenses always produce virtual images.

focal length

axis

F

Principal focus — point where rays hitting lens parallel to axis appear to all come from.

virtual rays

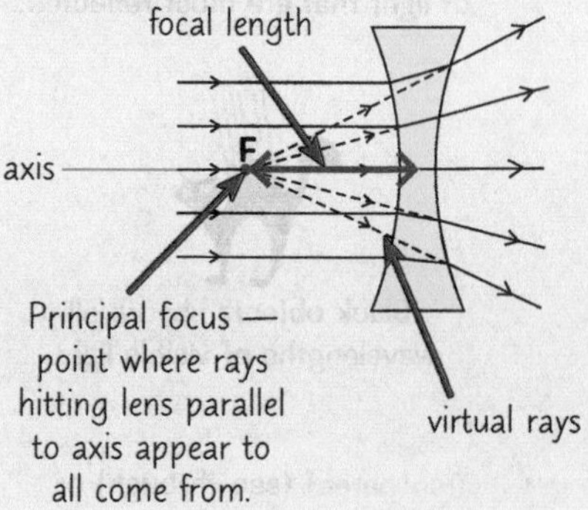

Lens Power

More powerful the lens:

- **More strongly it converges/ diverges rays of light**
- **Shorter the focal length**

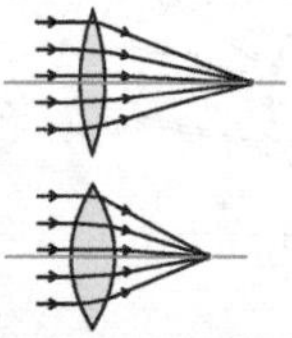

The more curved the lens surface, the more powerful the lens.

Converging lens = positive power. Diverging lens = negative power.

Ray Diagram for Diverging Lenses

Represents a diverging lens.

Ray travels parallel to axis, then refracts so it appears to have come from principal focus on the same side of the lens as the object.

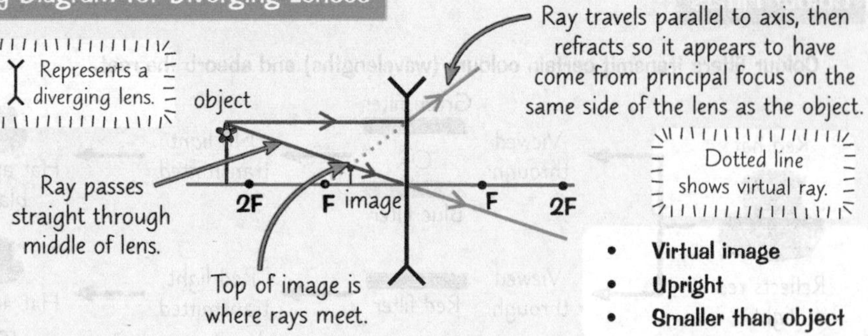

Dotted line shows virtual ray.

object

Ray passes straight through middle of lens.

2F   F   image   F   2F

Top of image is where rays meet.

- **Virtual image**
- **Upright**
- **Smaller than object**

Ray Diagrams & EM Waves

Four Ray Diagrams for Converging Lenses

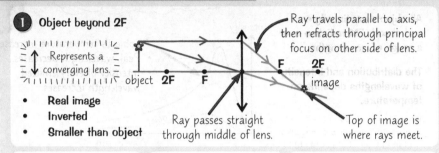

1 Object beyond 2F

Represents a converging lens.

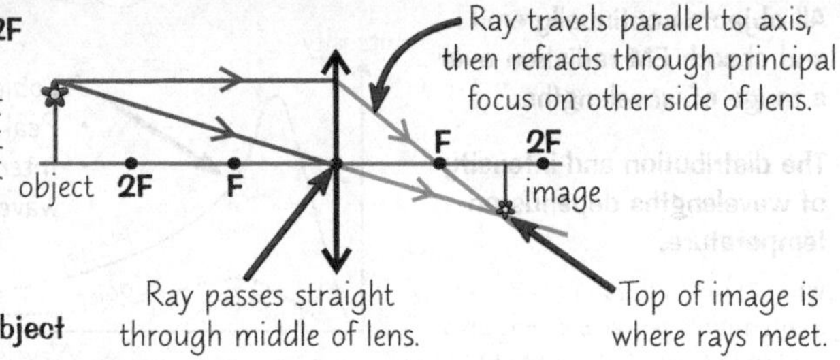

Ray travels parallel to axis, then refracts through principal focus on other side of lens.

object   2F   F   F   2F   image

- Real image
- Inverted
- Smaller than object

Ray passes straight through middle of lens.

Top of image is where rays meet.

2 At 2F

object

2F   F   F   2F

image

- Real image
- Inverted
- Same size as object

3 Between 2F and F

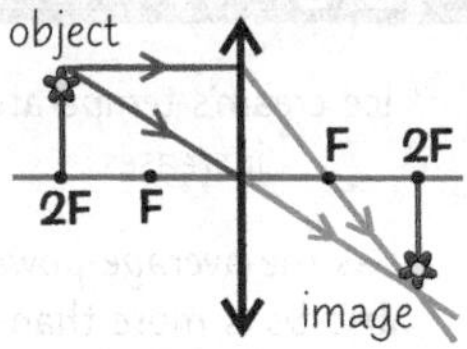

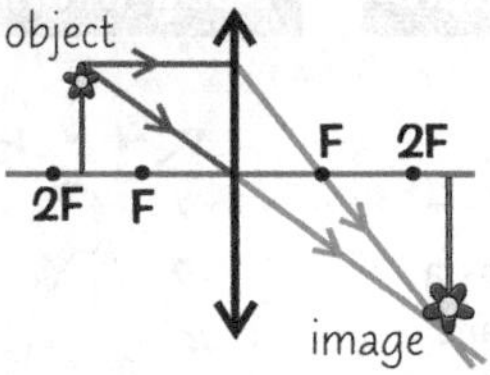

object

2F   F   F   2F

image

- Real image
- Inverted
- Bigger than object

4 Nearer than F

2F   F   F   2F
image   object

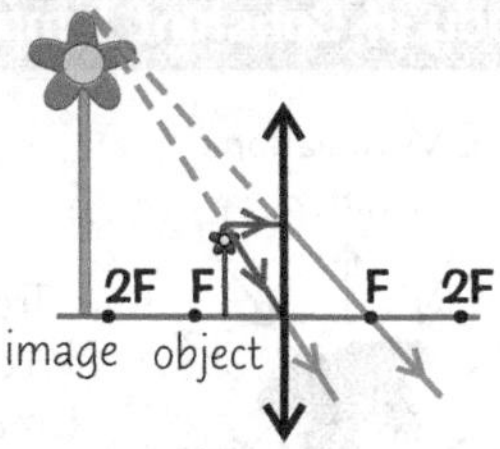

- Virtual image
- Upright
- Bigger than object

The Electromagnetic (EM) Spectrum

The EM spectrum is continuous.

red ⟶ violet

Radio waves	Microwaves	Infrared	Visible light	Ultraviolet	X-rays	Gamma rays

Increasing frequency, decreasing wavelength

Our eyes can only detect visible light.

EM waves:
- Transfer energy from source to absorber.
- Travel at same speed in a vacuum.

Changes in atoms and nuclei can...

...generate EM waves...

...be caused by absorption of EM waves...

...over a large frequency range.

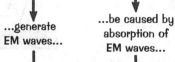

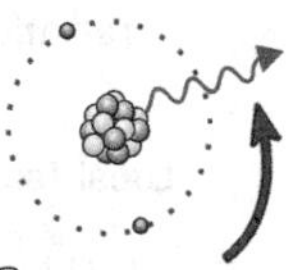

Gamma rays created by changes in atom's nucleus.

Emitting and Absorbing EM Radiation

Temperature and Radiation

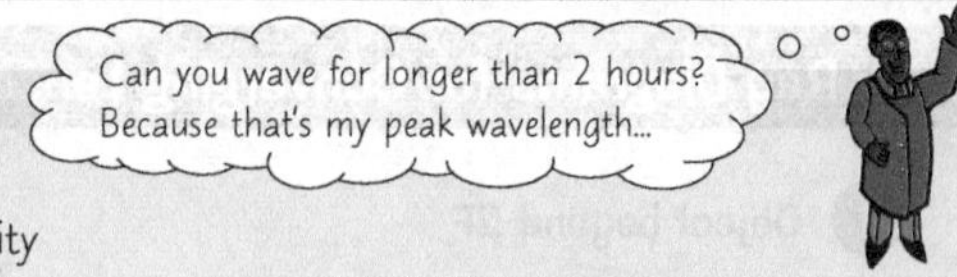
Can you wave for longer than 2 hours?
Because that's my peak wavelength...

All objects continually emit and absorb EM radiation over a range of wavelengths.

The distribution and intensity of wavelengths depends on temperature.

Intensity is power per unit area.

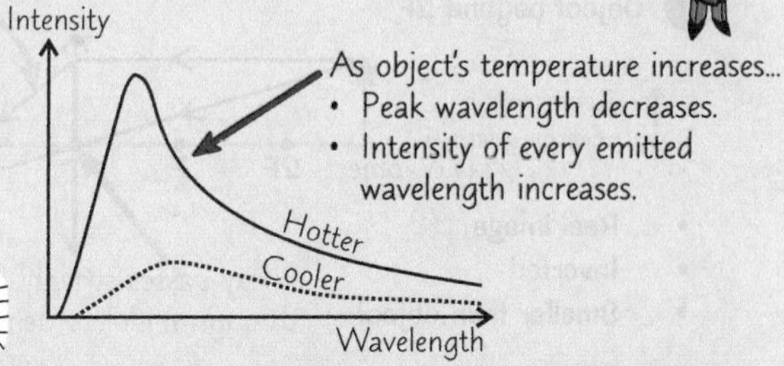
Intensity
As object's temperature increases...
• Peak wavelength decreases.
• Intensity of every emitted wavelength increases.
Hotter
Cooler
Wavelength

Body at Constant Temperature

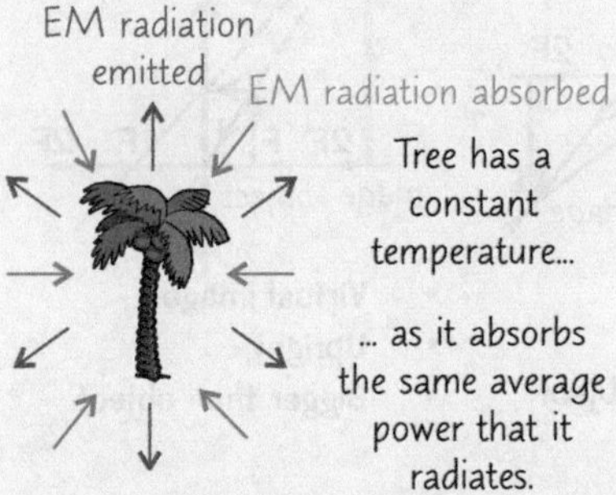
EM radiation emitted
EM radiation absorbed

Tree has a constant temperature...

... as it absorbs the same average power that it radiates.

Body that is Changing Temperature

Ice cream's temperature increases...

... as the average power it absorbs is more than the average power it radiates.

If average power absorbed is less than average power radiated, body's temperature decreases.

Radiation and Earth's Temperature

Daytime: Earth absorbs more radiation than it emits.

↓

Local temperature increases.

Nighttime: Earth emits more radiation than it absorbs.

↓

Local temperature decreases.

Overall, temperature of Earth remains fairly constant.

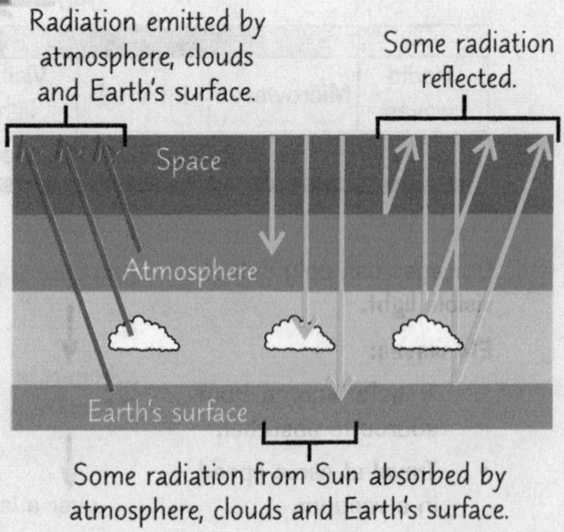
Radiation emitted by atmosphere, clouds and Earth's surface.
Some radiation reflected.
Space
Atmosphere
Earth's surface
Some radiation from Sun absorbed by atmosphere, clouds and Earth's surface.

Uses and Dangers of EM Waves

Producing Radio Waves

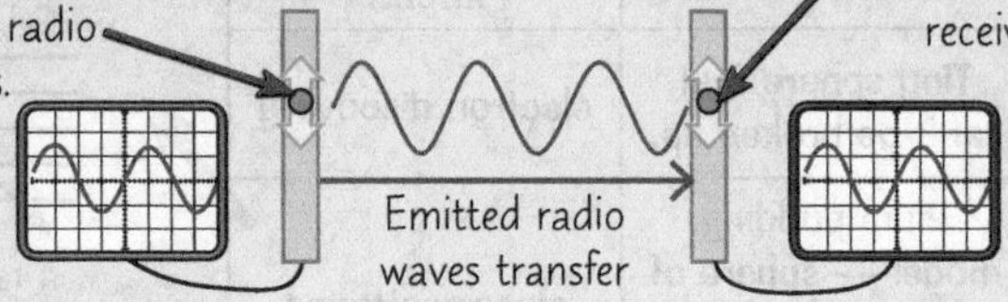
Electrons oscillate, producing radio waves.
transmitter
receiver
Radio waves absorbed, causing electrons in receiver to oscillate.
Alternating current supplied (shown on an oscilloscope).
Emitted radio waves transfer energy.
Alternating current of same frequency as radio waves induced in receiver.

Some Uses of EM Waves

Radio waves

- Broadcasting
- Communications
- Satellite transmissions

Microwaves

- Microwave ovens
- Communications
- Satellite transmissions

Visible light

- Photography
- Illumination
- Vision

Infrared radiation

- Electric heaters
- Cooking
- Thermal imaging
- Optical fibres
- Security systems
- TV remote controls
- Short range communications

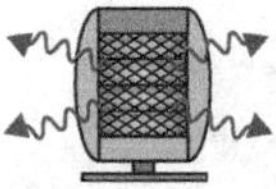

UV waves

- Fluorescent lamps
- Security marking
- Detecting forged bank notes
- Sterilising water

X-rays

- Medical X-rays
- Airport security scanners
- Looking inside objects

Gamma rays

- Detecting and treating cancer
- Sterilising food and medical equipment

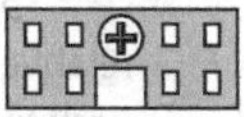

Dangers of EM Waves

<table>
<tr><th></th><th>Danger of excessive exposure</th></tr>
<tr><td>Microwaves</td><td>heats up cells</td></tr>
<tr><td>Infrared</td><td>causes skin burns</td></tr>
<tr><td>Ultraviolet</td><td>• causes damage to cells on surface of skin, which can lead to skin cancer
• damages eyes, possibly causing eye conditions or blindness</td></tr>
<tr><td>X-rays</td><td rowspan="2">causes cell damage or mutations, which can lead to cancer</td></tr>
<tr><td>Gamma rays</td></tr>
</table>

Types of ionising radiation. (Ultraviolet, X-rays, Gamma rays)

Frequency increases, possible danger increases

The Model of the Atom

The History of the Atom

		Developed further after...
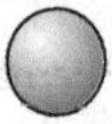	Tiny sphere that can't be broken up.	electron discovery
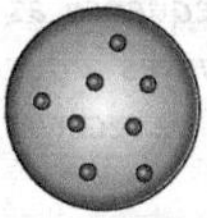	Plum pudding model — sphere of positive charge with negative electrons stuck in it.	alpha scattering experiment
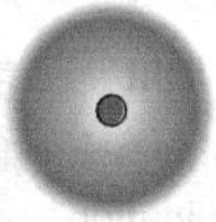	Nuclear model — positively charged nucleus surrounded by cloud of negative electrons.	Niels Bohr's theoretical calculations (that agreed with experimental data).
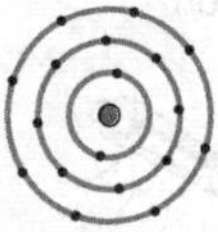	Bohr model — electrons orbit the nucleus at certain distances.	

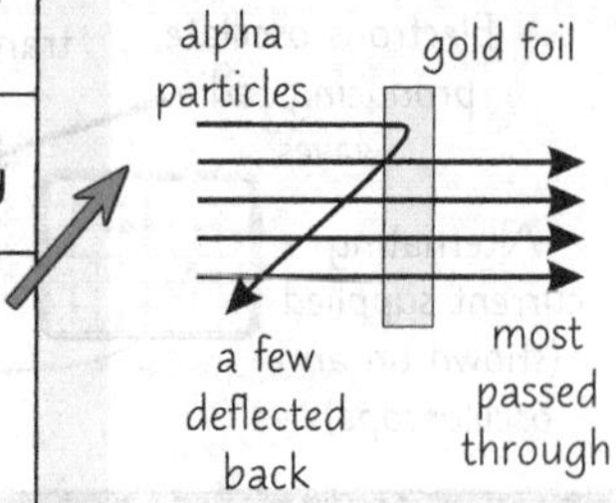
alpha particles
gold foil
a few deflected back
most passed through

Experiment showed:

- **Most of the mass of an atom is concentrated at a central, tiny nucleus.**
- **Nucleus is positively charged.**

The Current Model of the Atom

Size of atom ≈ 1×10^{-10} m.

- Small molecules are roughly the same size as an atom.
- The nucleus is much smaller than the atom.

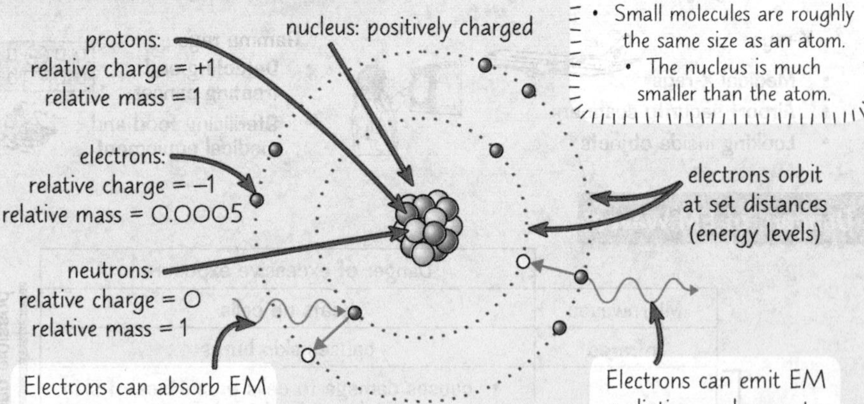
protons:
relative charge = +1
relative mass = 1
nucleus: positively charged
electrons:
relative charge = –1
relative mass = 0.0005
neutrons:
relative charge = 0
relative mass = 1
electrons orbit at set distances (energy levels)
Electrons can absorb EM radiation and move to higher energy levels.
Electrons can emit EM radiation and move to lower energy levels.

An atom's overall electric charge is zero as number of electrons = number of protons.
If an atom loses one or more electrons, it becomes a positively charged ion.

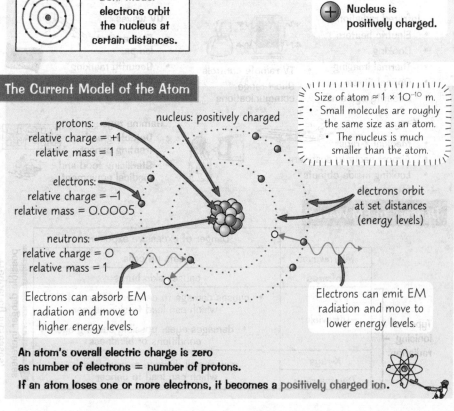

Isotopes and Radioactive Decay

Mass Number and Atomic Number

All atoms of each element have a set number of protons.

ISOTOPES of an element — atoms with the same number of protons but different numbers of neutrons (and so different masses).

MASS NUMBER — total number of protons and neutrons in an atom.

$^{16}_{8}O$

ATOMIC NUMBER — number of protons in an atom (equal to charge of nucleus).

Radioactive Decay

RADIOACTIVE DECAY — when the nucleus of an unstable isotope decays, giving out radiation to become more stable.

IONISING RADIATION (α, β^-, β^+ and γ) — radiation that knocks electrons off atoms, creating positive ions.

Unstable nuclei can also release neutrons (n) when they decay.

	alpha (α)	beta minus (β^-)	gamma (γ)
Consists of...	2 neutrons and 2 protons (helium nucleus)	fast-moving electron from nucleus	electromagnetic radiation from nucleus
Absorbed by...	Sheet of paper	Sheet of aluminium	Thick sheets of lead
Range in air	Few cm	Few metres	Long distances
Ionising power	Strong	Moderate	Weak

A positron (β^+) has same mass as an electron, but a relative charge of +1. It is ejected from the nucleus in β^+ decay.

Nuclear Equations

Mass and charge on each side of a nuclear equation must balance.

α-decay
- mass number decreases by 4
- atomic number decreases by 2

$$^{238}_{92}U \rightarrow {}^{234}_{90}Th + {}^{4}_{2}\alpha$$

(mass: −4; atomic: −2; $^{4}_{2}\alpha$ = alpha particle)

neutron emission
- mass no. decreases by 1
- atomic no. stays the same

γ-decay
- mass no. and atomic no. stay the same

When particles in nucleus rearrange due to decay, energy lost as gamma.

β^--decay
- mass no. stays the same
- atomic no. increases by 1 — a neutron turns into a proton

$$^{14}_{6}C \rightarrow {}^{14}_{7}N + {}^{0}_{-1}\beta$$

(mass: no change; atomic: +1; $^{0}_{-1}\beta$ = electron)

β^+-decay
- mass no. stays the same
- atomic no. decreases by 1 — a proton turns into a neutron

$$^{18}_{9}F \rightarrow {}^{18}_{8}O + {}^{0}_{1}\beta$$

(mass: no change; atomic: −1; $^{0}_{1}\beta$ = positron)

You don't need to know these exact equations, just how mass and atomic numbers change during decays.

Radioactivity

Activity

Radioactive decays can be detected by photographic film.

Radioactive decay is random.
Can't say if or when a nucleus will decay.

ACTIVITY — the rate at which a source decays, measured in becquerels (Bq).

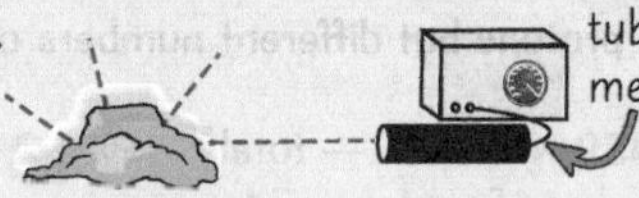
A Geiger-Muller tube and counter measures activity.

Background Radiation

BACKGROUND RADIATION — low-level radiation that's always around us.

Two types of sources:

1. **From Earth — rocks, food, air, building materials, nuclear waste, fallout from nuclear explosions.**
2. **From space — cosmic rays.**

Contamination and Irradiation

RADIOACTIVE CONTAMINATION — getting unwanted radioactive atoms onto or into an object.

IRRADIATION — the exposure of an object to ionising radiation (doesn't make the object radioactive).

Half-life

HALF-LIFE — time taken for the number of nuclei of an isotope in a sample to halve.

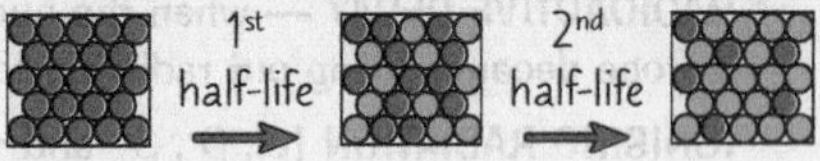
1st half-life
2nd half-life

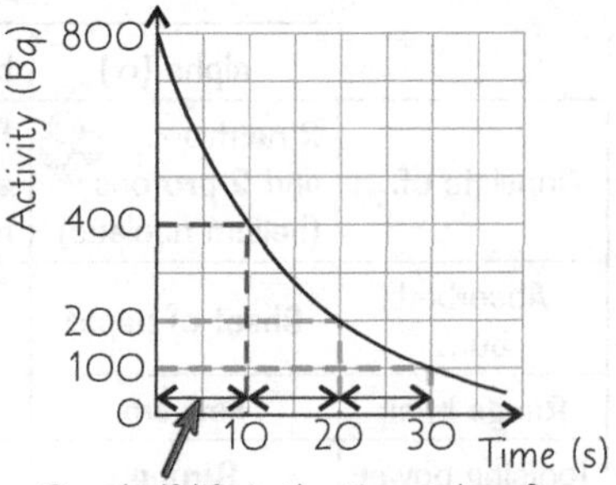

One half-life is the time taken for the activity of a sample to halve.

Risk of Radiation

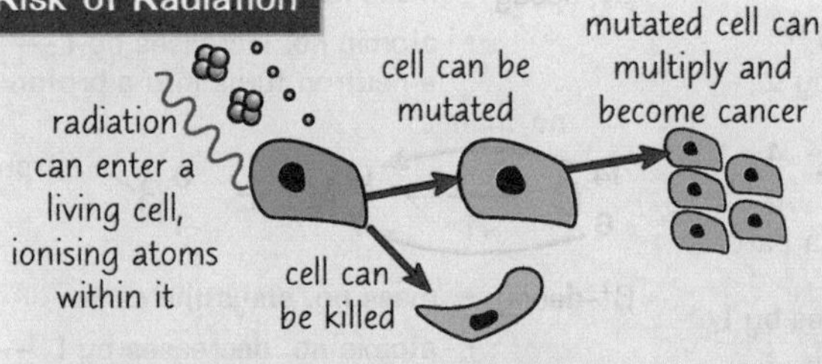
radiation can enter a living cell, ionising atoms within it
cell can be mutated
mutated cell can multiply and become cancer
cell can be killed

Inside body:
- **α is most dangerous**
- **γ is least dangerous**

Outside body:
- **γ is most dangerous**
- **α is least dangerous**

Three precautions to reduce exposure:

1. **Keep sources in lead-lined boxes.**
2. **Stand behind barriers or be in a different room to the source.**
3. **Wear protective clothing and use tongs to handle sources.**

People exposed to radiation (e.g. hospital staff and patients) should have their exposure limited.

Uses of Radiation

Half-life and Hazards

Short half-life ⟹ activity falls quickly ⟹ emits high amounts of radiation in short time ⟹ quickly becomes safe

Long half-life ⟹ activity falls slowly ⟹ emits small amounts of radiation over long time ⟹ hazardous for a longer time

Thickness Gauging

β⁻ partially absorbed by thin materials (e.g. paper).

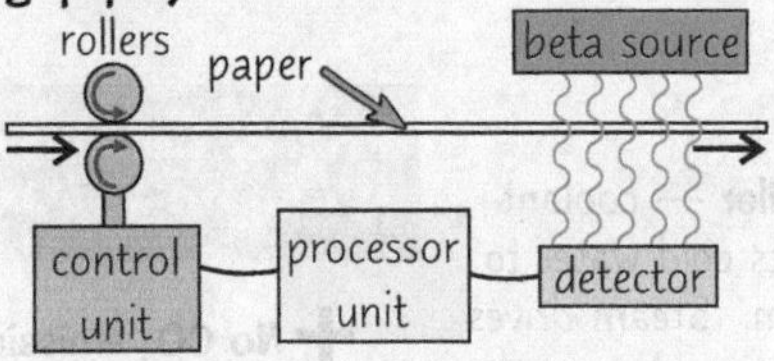

If amount of detected radiation changes, thickness has changed, so rollers adjusted.

Two Ways to Treat Cancer

1. Externally — gamma sources from outside body directed at cancer cells.

2. Internally — alpha and beta sources put inside body next to cancer cells.

Treatments cause damage to both cancerous and healthy cells.

Medical Tracers

Medical tracer (radioactive source) injected or swallowed to explore internal organs.

Radiation detected outside the body.

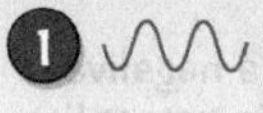

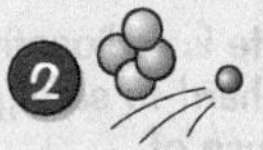

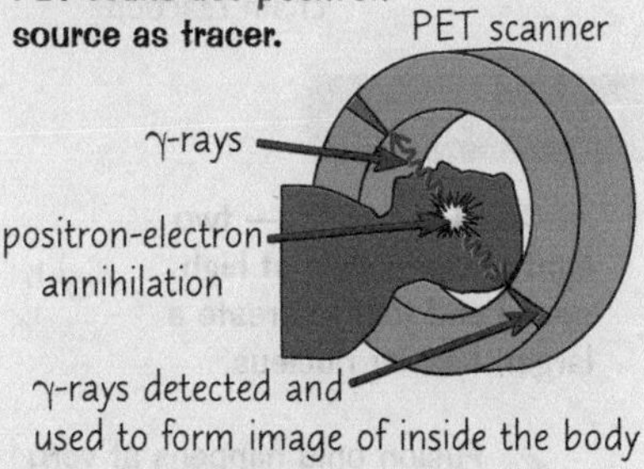

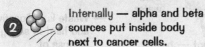

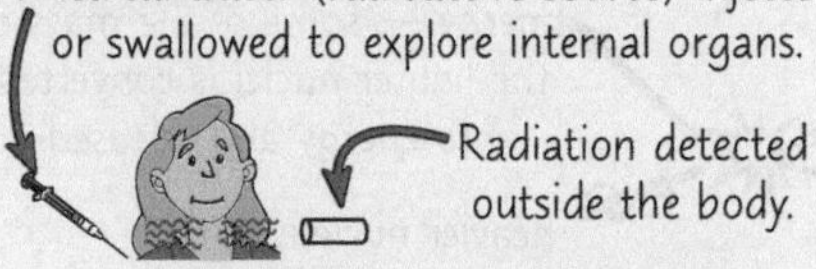

Gamma sources used so that radiation passes out of body without causing much damage.

Fire Alarms

Alpha source in fire alarm causes ionisation and current.

Smoke particles stop the current, and cause alarm to sound.

Sterilisation

High doses of gamma kills microbes.

So gamma radiation used to sterilise food and medical equipment.

not sterilised ← gamma source → sterilised

PET Scans

PET scans use positron source as tracer.

PET scanner
γ-rays
positron-electron annihilation
γ-rays detected and used to form image of inside the body

Positron sources have very short half-lives, so must be produced nearby.

Both of these can be used to diagnose medical conditions, e.g. cancer.

Nuclear Fission and Fusion

Nuclear Fission

NUCLEAR FISSION — splitting a large, unstable nucleus into two smaller nuclei of approximately equal size.

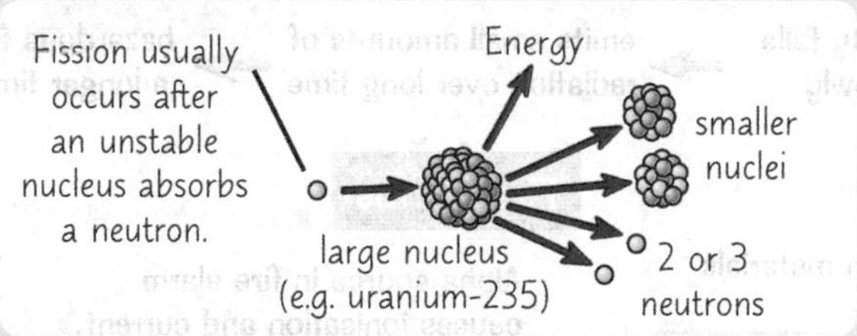
Fission usually occurs after an unstable nucleus absorbs a neutron.
Energy
smaller nuclei
large nucleus (e.g. uranium-235)
2 or 3 neutrons

Released neutrons can be absorbed by another nucleus, starting a chain reaction...

... controlled in nuclear reactor.

Nuclear Reactors

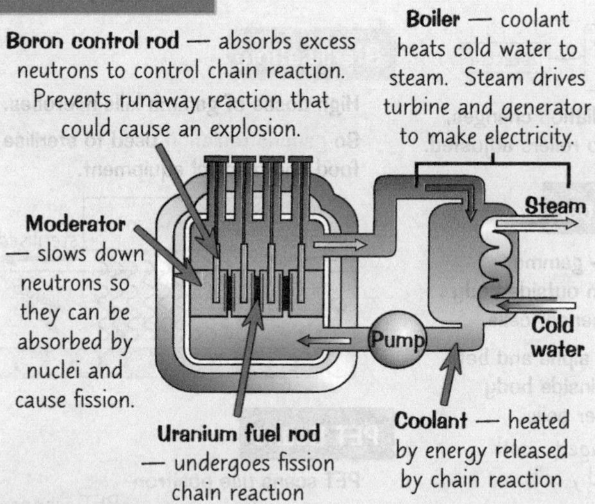
Boron control rod — absorbs excess neutrons to control chain reaction. Prevents runaway reaction that could cause an explosion.
Boiler — coolant heats cold water to steam. Steam drives turbine and generator to make electricity.
Moderator — slows down neutrons so they can be absorbed by nuclei and cause fission.
Steam
Pump
Cold water
Uranium fuel rod — undergoes fission chain reaction
Coolant — heated by energy released by chain reaction

Pros & Cons of Nuclear Power

- **+ No CO_2 emissions**
- **+ A lot of energy from small amount of fuel**
- **+ Reliable**
- **− Has a negative public perception**
- **− Waste is radioactive and hard to safely dispose of**
- **− Risk of catastrophe**

Nuclear Fusion

NUCLEAR FUSION — two light nuclei collide at high speed and join to create a larger, heavier nucleus.

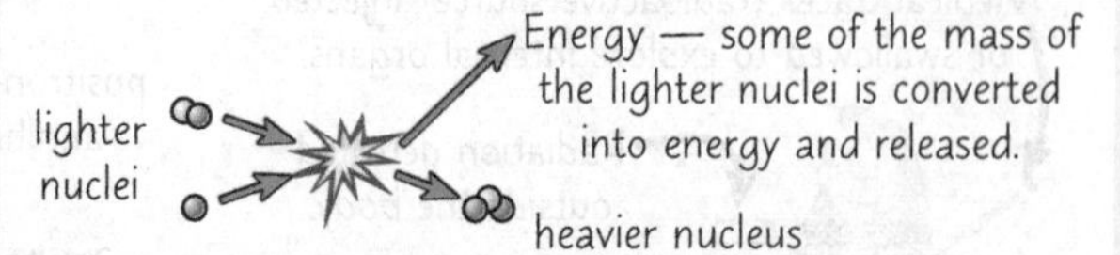
lighter nuclei
Energy — some of the mass of the lighter nuclei is converted into energy and released.
heavier nucleus

Fusion only happens at very high temperature and pressure, as nuclei have to overcome electrostatic repulsion to get close enough to fuse.

Making these conditions on Earth needs a lot of energy and is very expensive... ... so not yet built an efficient fusion power station.

The Solar System and Gravity

Our Solar System

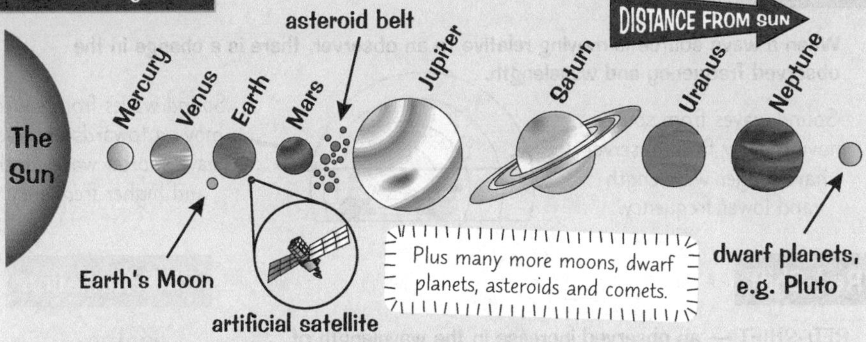
asteroid belt
DISTANCE FROM SUN
The Sun
Mercury
Venus
Earth
Mars
Jupiter
Saturn
Uranus
Neptune
Earth's Moon
artificial satellite
Plus many more moons, dwarf planets, asteroids and comets.
dwarf planets, e.g. Pluto

- The eight planets orbit the Sun (our star) in almost circular orbits.
- Moons are natural satellites that orbit planets.
  Our moon orbits Earth in almost circular orbit.
- Artificial satellites usually orbit the Earth in fairly circular orbits.
- Comets orbit the Sun in highly elliptical orbits. They travel faster closer to the Sun.

Changing Ideas of the Solar System

1000s of years ago	Geocentric model 	Everything orbits around Earth.
Now	Heliocentric model 	Planets orbit Sun.

Gravitational Field Strength

Gravitational field strength, g, of a body (e.g. a planet) depends on two things:

1. 

Mass of the body. Larger mass = bigger g.
2. 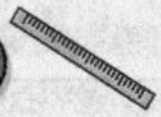 Distance from it. Further away = smaller g.

Weight is directly proportional to g. A mass has different weights on different bodies.

Circular Orbits

Gravitational force keeps planets and satellites in circular orbits.

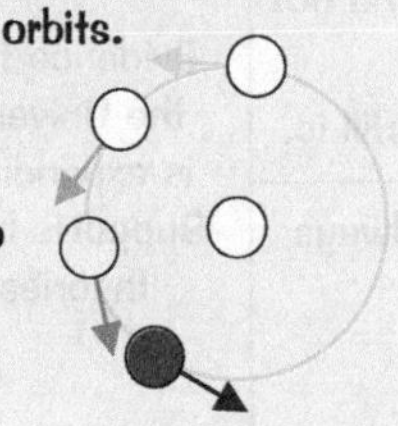

It causes the object's direction to constantly change.

This means the object's velocity constantly changes.

The object's speed remains constant.

Stable Orbits

If the speed of an object in a stable orbit changes, the radius (size) of the orbit changes.

The smaller the orbit radius, the faster the object must travel.

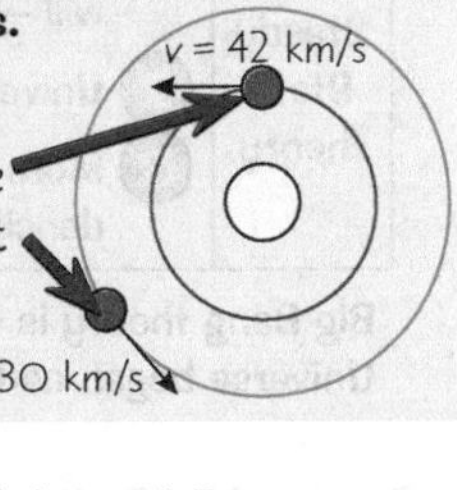
v = 42 km/s
v = 30 km/s

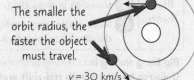

The Universe: Theories & Evidence

Doppler Effect

When a wave source is moving relative to an observer, there is a change in the observed frequency and wavelength.

Sound waves from source moving away from observer have longer wavelength and lower frequency.

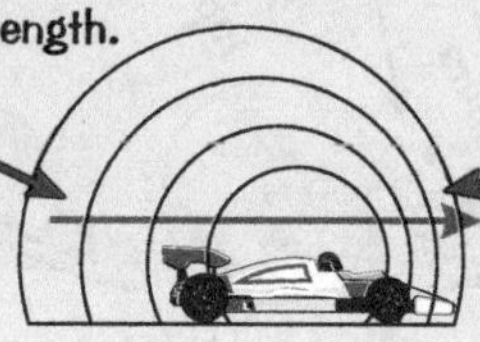

Sound waves from source moving towards observer have shorter wavelength and higher frequency.

Red-Shift

RED-SHIFT — an observed increase in the wavelength of light (light is shifted towards the red end of the spectrum). Observed when a galaxy moves away from the Earth.

The more distant the galaxy:

- the faster it moves away from us
- the greater its red-shift

The light observed from most galaxies is red-shifted, so most galaxies are moving away from us.

CMB Radiation

COSMIC MICROWAVE BACKGROUND (CMB) RADIATION — low frequency electromagnetic radiation coming from all parts of the Universe.

Cosmic maaaaaan!

Two Theories for the Creation of the Universe

Theory	Three things the theory says about the Universe	Red-shift	CMB radiation
Big Bang theory	**1 Universe has finite age.** **2 All matter started in a dense and hot tiny space and 'exploded'.** **3 Space started expanding and still is.**	**Evidence that the Universe is expanding. Supports both theories.**	**Evidence the Universe had a beginning. Supports Big Bang theory.**
Steady State theory	**1 Universe always existed and always will — no beginning or end.** **2 Universe is expanding.** **3 More matter constantly created — density stays constant.**		**Can't be explained. Doesn't support Steady State theory.**

Big Bang theory is currently accepted model for how the Universe began as both red-shift and CMB radiation support it.

Stars and Looking into Space

The Life Cycle of a Star

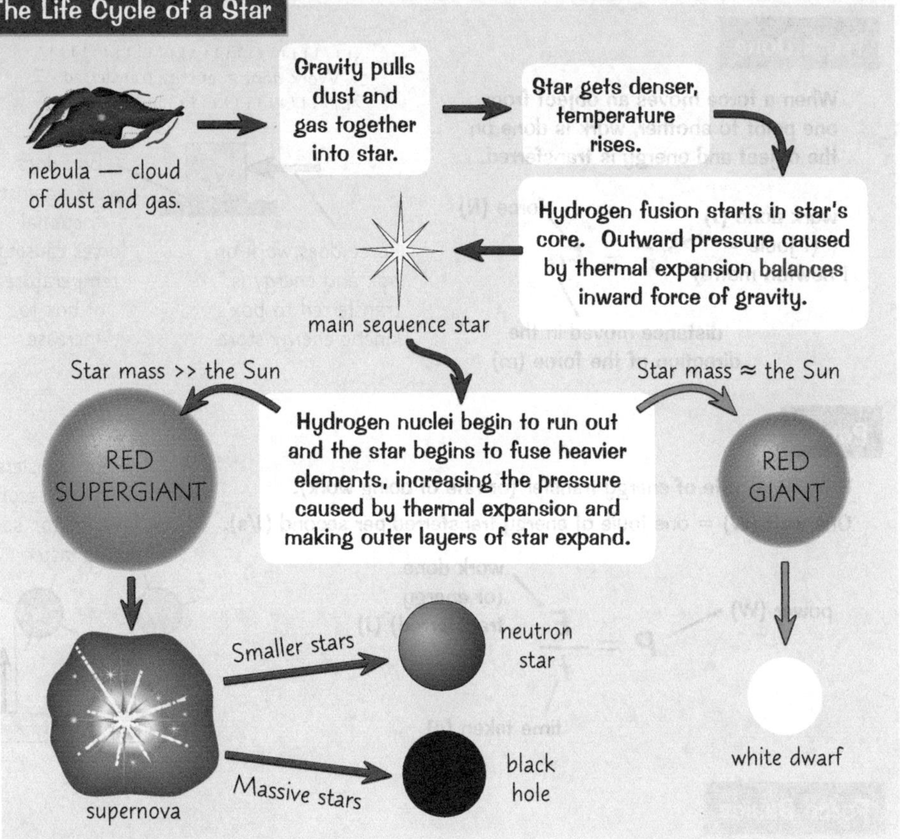
nebula — cloud of dust and gas.
Gravity pulls dust and gas together into star.
Star gets denser, temperature rises.
Hydrogen fusion starts in star's core. Outward pressure caused by thermal expansion balances inward force of gravity.
main sequence star
Hydrogen nuclei begin to run out and the star begins to fuse heavier elements, increasing the pressure caused by thermal expansion and making outer layers of star expand.
Star mass >> the Sun
RED SUPERGIANT
supernova
Smaller stars
neutron star
Massive stars
black hole
Star mass ≈ the Sun
RED GIANT
white dwarf

Observing the Universe

From 1600s

Optical **telescopes:**

- **First telescopes**
- **Only detect visible light**

From 1930s

Telescopes for other EM waves (e.g. Radio and X-ray).

From 1960s

Telescopes put into space.

Two reasons to put telescopes into space:

1. **To avoid light/air pollution.**
2. **To detect EM waves that would be absorbed by Earth's atmosphere.**

Telescopes and computers improved over time to give better resolution/magnification and sharper images.

Work Done, Power and Forces

Most of the stuff on pages 12-14 can also be assessed as part of this section (and so can be tested on papers 1 and 2).

Work Done

Work done = energy transferred.

When a force moves an object from one point to another, work is done on the object and energy is transferred.

$$E = Fd$$

- **work done (J)** (1 joule = 1 newton metre)
- **force (N)**
- **distance moved in the direction of the force (m)**

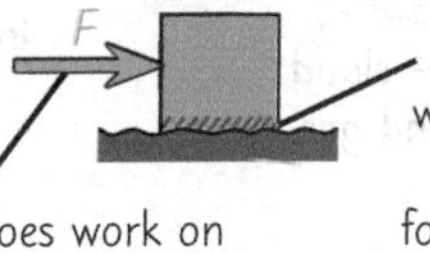
F
Force does work on box and energy is transferred to box's kinetic energy store.
Box does work against frictional forces causing temperature of box to increase.

Power

POWER — rate of energy transfer (or rate of doing work).

One watt (W) = one joule of energy transferred per second (J/s).

$$P = \frac{E}{t}$$

- **power (W)**
- **work done (or energy transferred) (J)**
- **time taken (s)**

2 W motor transfers more energy per second than 1 W motor, so lifts mass faster.

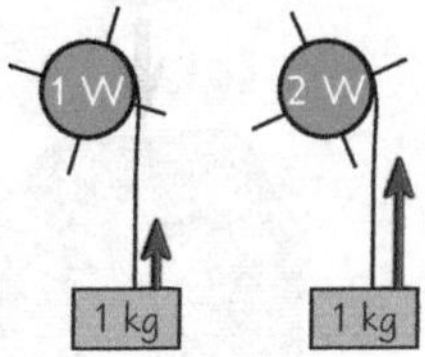

Force Basics

FORCE — a push or a pull on an object caused by it interacting with something.

When two objects interact, they exert an equal but opposite force on each other.

This pair of forces is an interaction pair.

Two types of forces:

1. **Contact forces: objects have to be touching.**

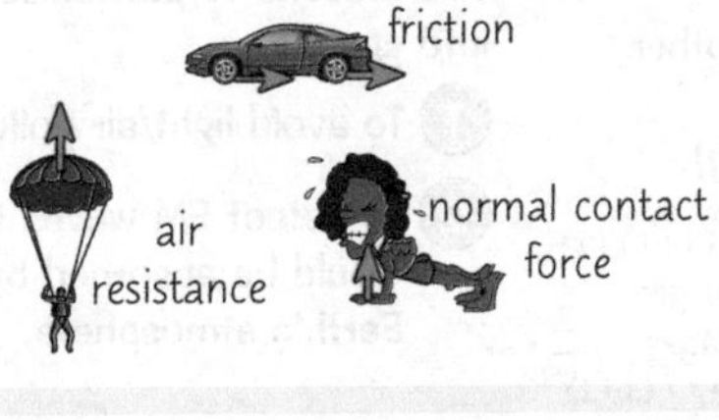
friction
air resistance
normal contact force

2. **Non-contact forces: objects don't need to be touching.**

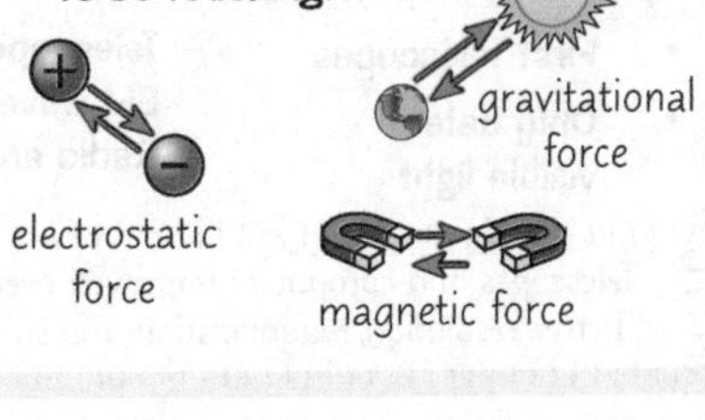
gravitational force
electrostatic force
magnetic force

Forces

The stuff on scalars and vectors on page 6 can also be assessed in this section.

Vectors

Forces, and other vectors, can be represented visually as arrows.

Direction of arrow shows direction of quantity.
Length of arrow shows magnitude.

Free Body Force Diagrams

FREE BODY FORCE DIAGRAM — shows all forces acting on an isolated body.

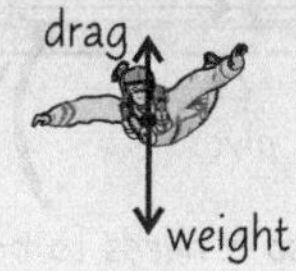

Arrows show relative magnitudes and directions of forces acting.

Equilibrium

EQUILIBRIUM — when the forces acting on an object are balanced and the resultant force is zero.

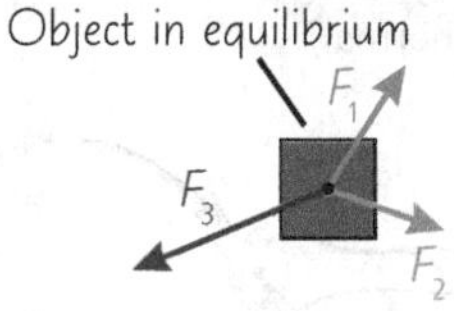

Drawing forces tip-to-tail in scale drawing creates a closed loop.

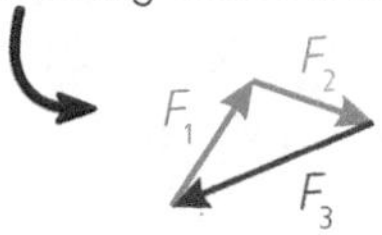

Resolving Forces

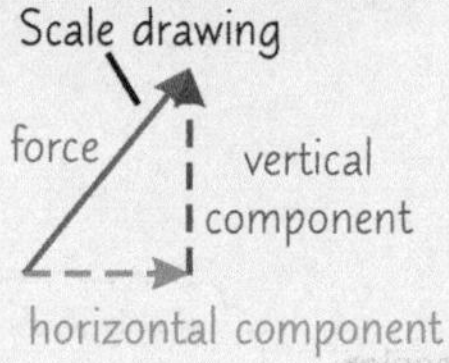

Component forces acting together have same effect as the single force.

Two Ways to Calculate Resultant Force

RESULTANT (NET) FORCE — a single force that can replace all the forces acting on an object to give the same effect as all the original forces acting together.

1. Add forces pointing in same direction. Subtract forces pointing in opposite directions.

$F_1 - F_2$ = resultant force

2. 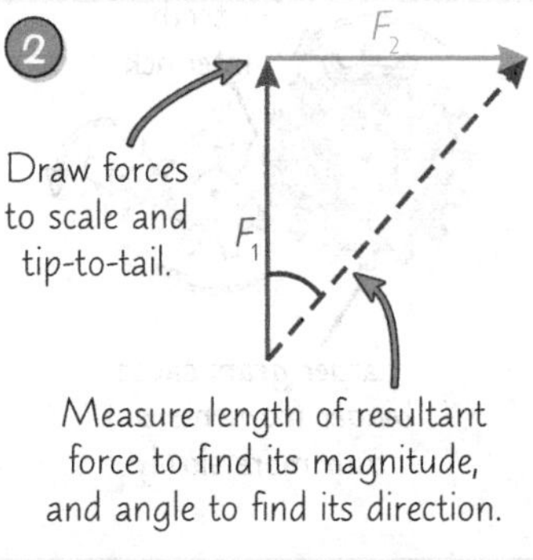

Moments

Calculating Moments

MOMENT — the turning effect of a force.

$$\text{moment of a force (Nm)} = \text{force (N)} \times \text{distance normal to the direction of the force (m)}$$

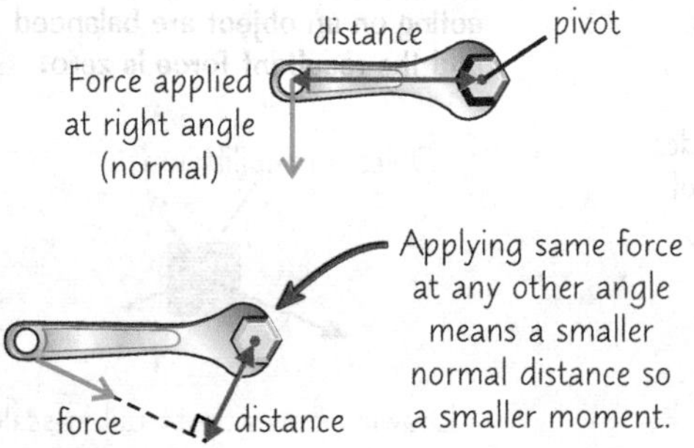
distance
pivot
Force applied at right angle (normal)
Applying same force at any other angle means a smaller normal distance so a smaller moment.
force
distance

Moments in Equilibrium

PRINCIPLE OF MOMENTS — If object is in equilibrium, sum of clockwise moments = sum of anticlockwise moments about a pivot.

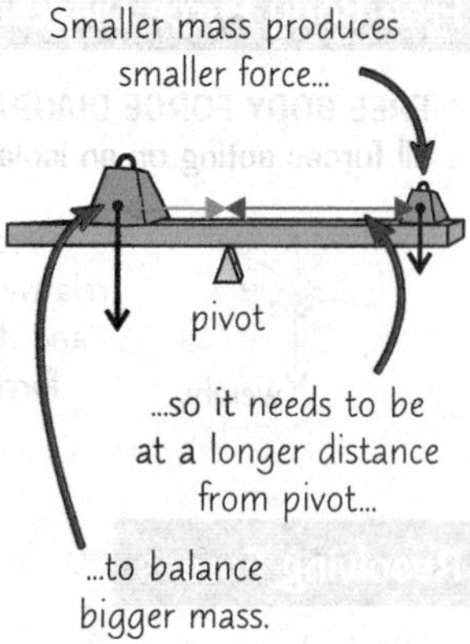
Smaller mass produces smaller force...
pivot
...so it needs to be at a longer distance from pivot...
...to balance bigger mass.

Gears

GEARS — used to transmit the rotational effect of a force from one place to another.

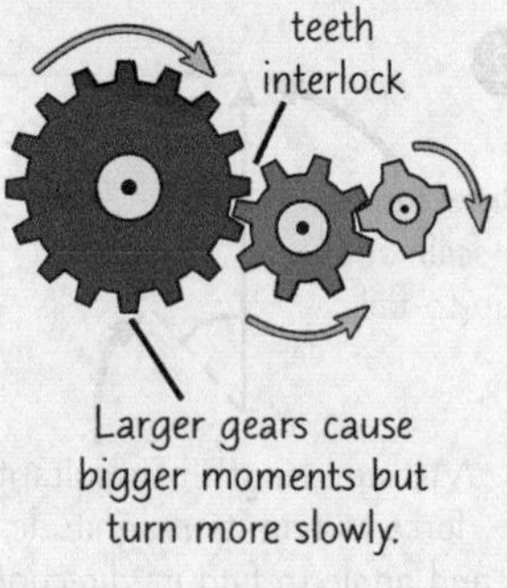
teeth interlock
Larger gears cause bigger moments but turn more slowly.

Levers

LEVERS — make it easier to do work e.g. lift a load.

If only levers made doing revision easier...

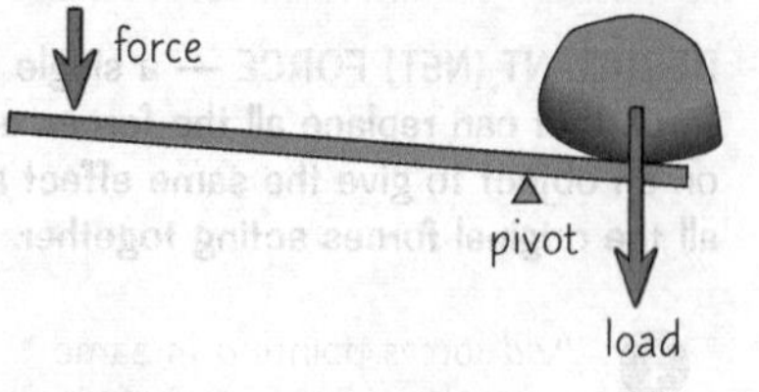
force
pivot
load

Increasing distance between pivot and applied force. → **Less force required to get the same moment.** → **Easier to lift load.**

Current and Circuits

Some of the stuff in 'The Current Model of the Atom' box on page 26 can also be assessed as part of this section.

Current

ELECTRIC CURRENT — the rate of flow of charge.

$$Q = It$$

charge (coulombs, C), **current (amperes, A)**, **time (s)**

In metals, current is caused by a flow of electrons.

Current in Circuits

no source of potential difference

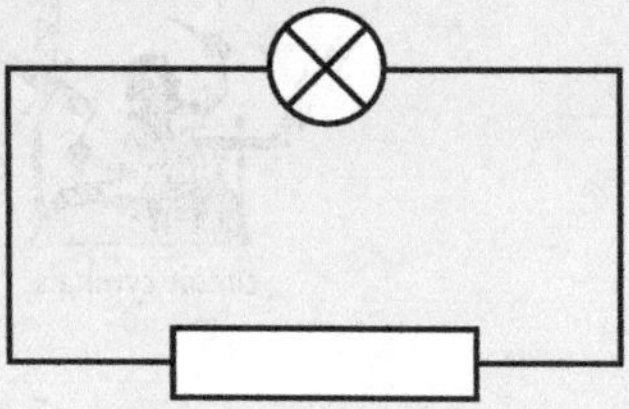

no current flows

source of potential difference (battery)

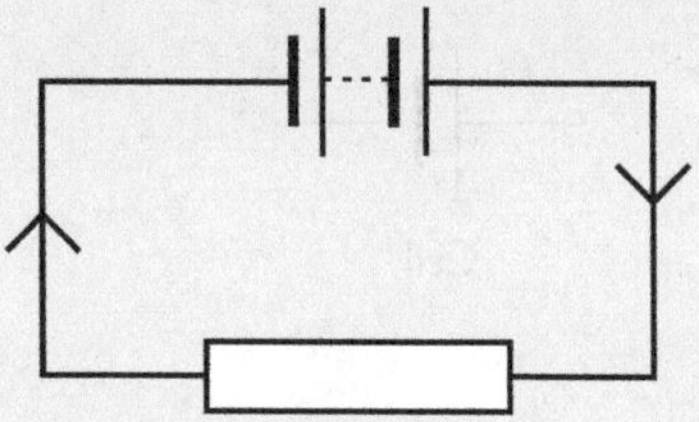

current flows

Current through Components

$$V = IR$$

potential difference (volts, V), **current (amperes, A)**, **resistance (ohms, Ω)**

Resistance is anything that slows down the flow of charge.

Current through a component depends on the component's resistance and the potential difference (p.d.) across the component.

The greater the resistance, the smaller the current (at a fixed p.d.).

Use a variable resistor to change the current in a circuit:

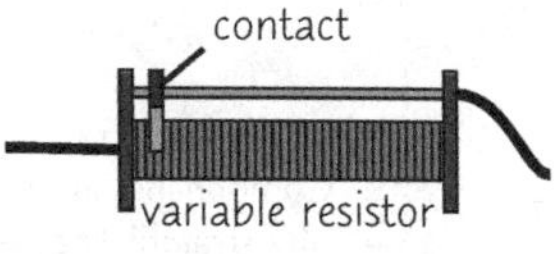

Lower resistance, greater current

slide contact other way

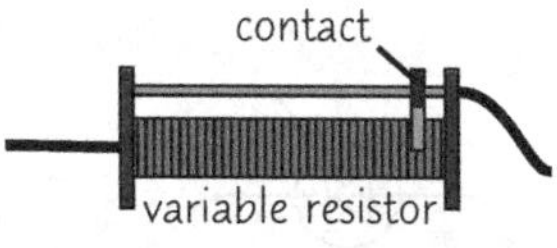

Higher resistance, lower current

Potential Difference & Circuit Symbols

Potential Difference

POTENTIAL DIFFERENCE — the energy transferred per unit of charge that passes between two points in a circuit.

Potential difference can also be called voltage.

Energy, Charge and P.d. Equation

$$E = QV$$

- E — Energy transferred (J)
- Q — charge moved (C)
- V — potential difference (V)

1 volt (V) = 1 joule per coulomb (J/C)

Circuit Symbols

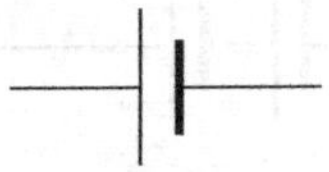
Cell

Battery

circuit cymbals

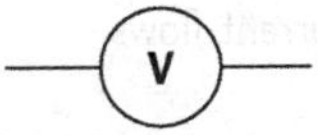
Voltmeter

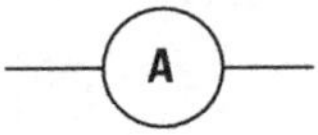
Ammeter

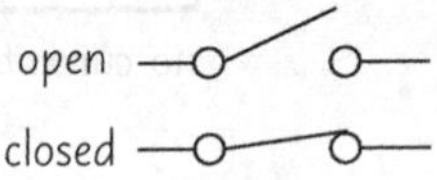

Switch

Resistor

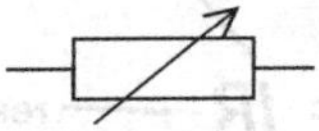
Variable resistor

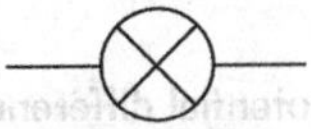
Filament lamp (or bulb)

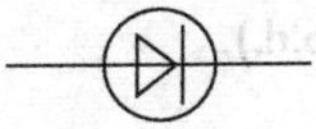
Diode

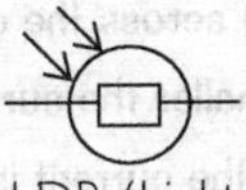
LDR (Light-Dependent Resistor)

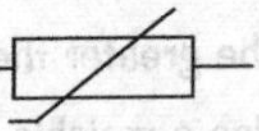
Thermistor

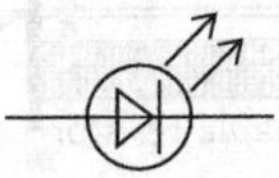
LED (Light-Emitting Diode)

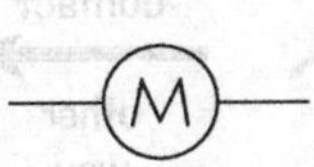
Motor

Components are connected by straight lines — they represent the wires.

Components of Circuits

Three Different Current-Potential Difference Graphs

1 A fixed resistor at constant temperature 

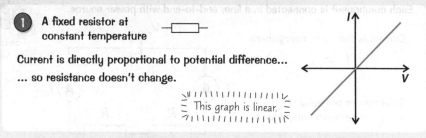

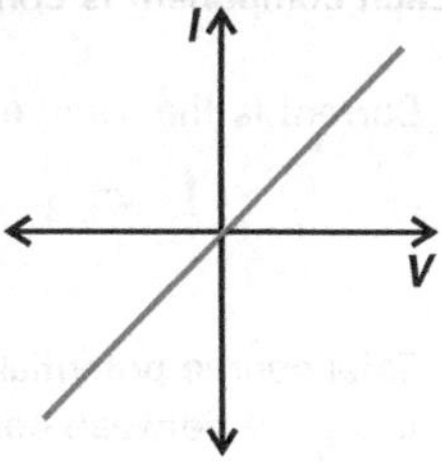

Current is directly proportional to potential difference...

... so resistance doesn't change.

This graph is linear.

Components with changing resistance (when current through them varies):

2 Filament lamp 

Current increases...

... so temperature of filament increases...

... so resistance increases.

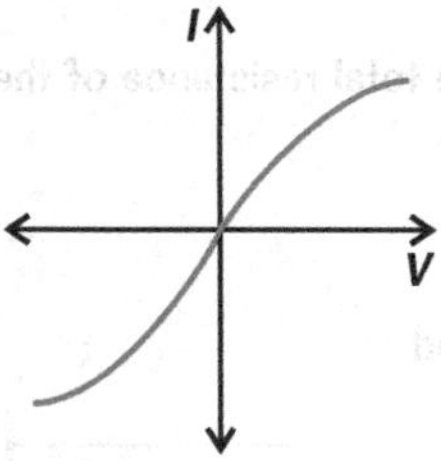

3 Diode 

High resistance in one direction...

... so current only flows in the other direction.

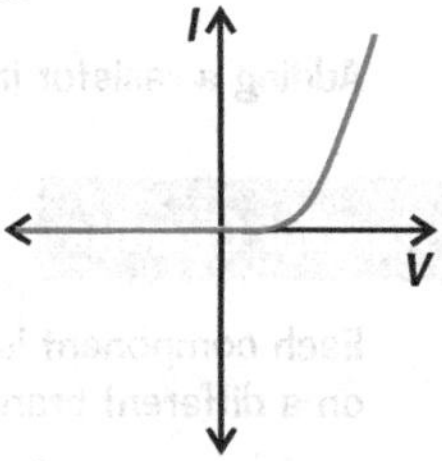

These graphs are non-linear.

LDRs and Thermistors

	LDR 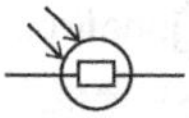	Thermistor 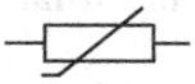
Resistance depends on...	light intensity	temperature
Lower resistance in...	brighter light	hotter temperatures
Resistance graphs...	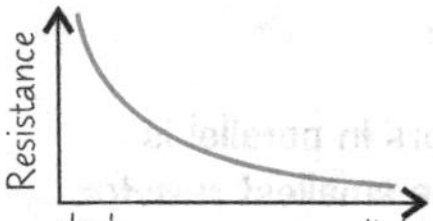	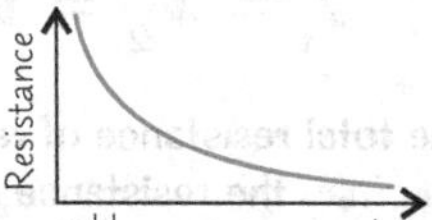

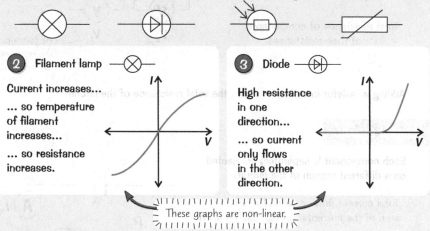

Series and Parallel Circuits

Serious Sir Kitten

Series Circuits

Each component is connected in a line, end-to-end with power source.

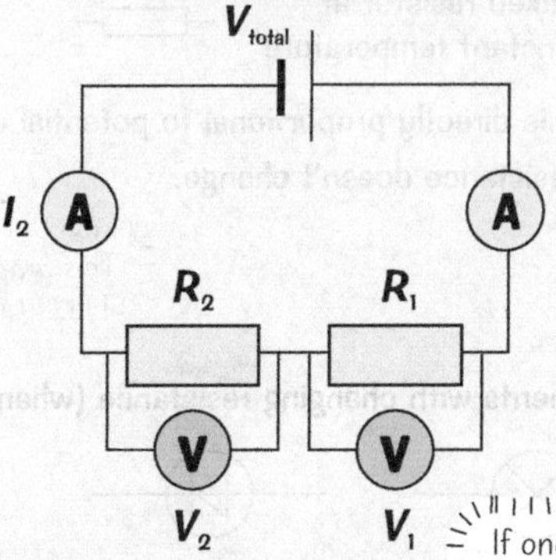

Current is the same everywhere.

$$I_1 = I_2$$

Total source potential difference is shared between components.

$$V_{total} = V_1 + V_2$$

Total resistance of components = sum of their resistances.

$$R_{total} = R_1 + R_2$$

If one component breaks, no current flows in circuit.

Adding a resistor in series increases the total resistance of the circuit.

Parallel Circuits

Each component is separately connected on a different branch of the circuit.

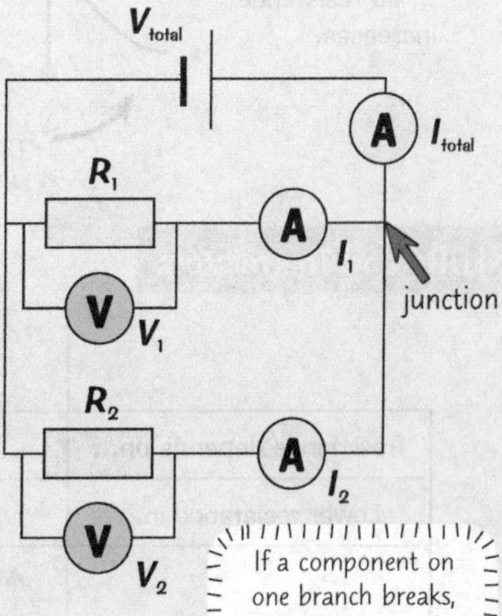

Total current flowing around a circuit = sum of the currents through each branch.

$$I_{total} = I_1 + I_2$$

The total current entering a junction equals the total current leaving the junction.

Potential difference across each branch is the same as the source potential difference.

$$V_1 = V_2 = V_{total}$$

If a component on one branch breaks, components on other branches still work as current still flows through them.

The total resistance of resistors in parallel is less than the resistance of the smallest resistor.

Adding a resistor in parallel decreases the total resistance of the circuit.

Energy and Power in Circuits

Energy Transfers

When charge flows, work is done (and so energy is transferred).

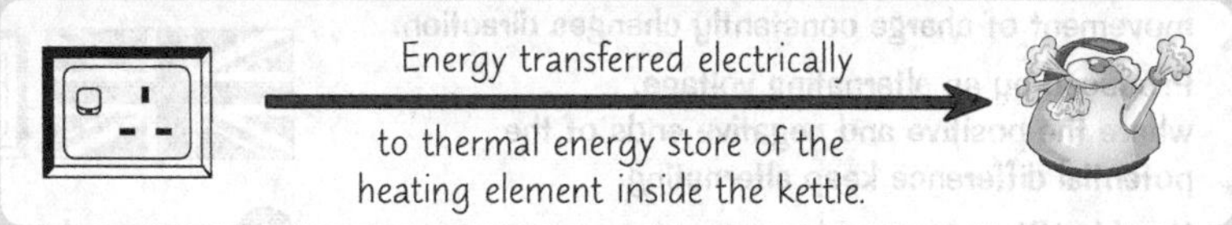
Energy transferred electrically
to thermal energy store of the heating element inside the kettle.

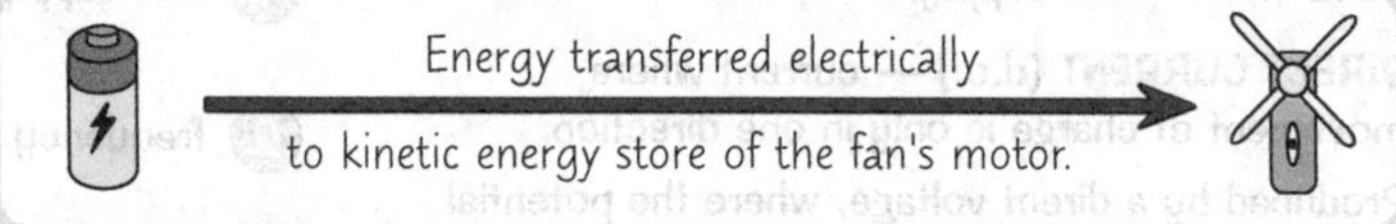
Energy transferred electrically
to kinetic energy store of the fan's motor.

Dissipated Energy in Circuits

Some energy is dissipated to thermal energy stores when a current does work against resistance. This has a heating effect.

Current flows through a resistor → **Electrons collide with, and transfer energy to, the lattice of ions in the resistor** → **Ions vibrate more, so energy in thermal energy store increases** → **The resistor heats up**

Advantage of heating effect — e.g. used in electric heaters, toasters, etc.

Disadvantage of heating effect — e.g. causes energy losses in circuits.

Low resistance wires used to reduce energy losses in circuits.

Energy and Power

POWER — energy transferred per second.

$$P = \frac{E}{t}$$

power (watt, W), **energy transferred (J)**, **time taken (s)**

A power rating of an appliance is the maximum amount of energy transferred between stores per second when the appliance is in use.

Calculating Power

The higher the current through or potential difference across a device, the greater its power.

$$P = IV$$

electrical power (W), **current (A)**, **potential difference (V)**

$$P = I^2R$$

electrical power (W), **current (A)**, **resistance (Ω)**

Electricity at Home

Two Types of Electricity Supply

1. **ALTERNATING CURRENT (a.c.) — current where movement of charge constantly changes direction.**
   Produced by an alternating voltage, where the positive and negative ends of the potential difference keep alternating.
   Used in UK mains supply.
2. **DIRECT CURRENT (d.c.) — current where movement of charge is only in one direction.**
   Produced by a direct voltage, where the potential difference is only positive or negative, not both.
   Supplied by cells and batteries.

Three Facts about UK Mains Supply

1. **a.c. supply**
2. **frequency of 50 Hz**
3. **voltage around 230 V**

Three-core Cables

	live wire	neutral wire	earth wire
Function	Provides alternating potential difference from mains supply.	Completes the circuit.	Safety — stops appliance casing becoming live.

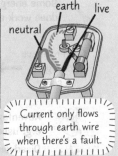

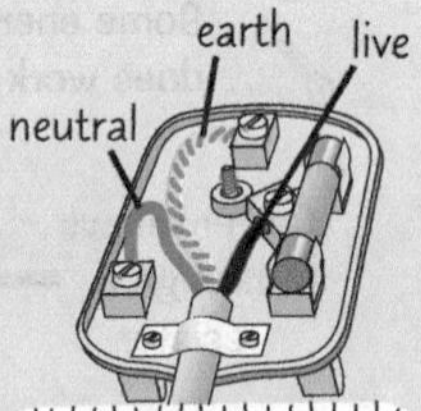

Current only flows through earth wire when there's a fault.

- **Potential difference between live wire and neutral or earth wires = 230 V.**
- **Potential difference between neutral and earth wire = 0 V.**

Electric Shocks and Safety

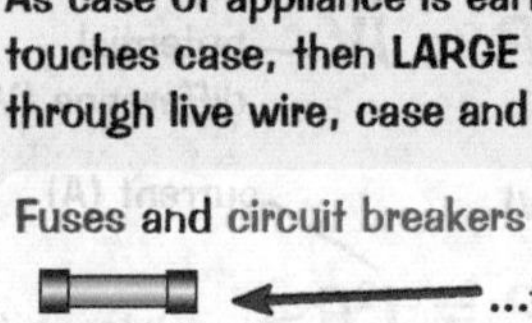

Large potential difference produced across body. → **Current flows through body.** →

Electric shock — injury or even death.

As case of appliance is earthed, if live wire touches case, then LARGE current surges through live wire, case and earth wire.

Any connection between the live wire and the earth can be dangerous — e.g. it could cause a fire.

Fuses and circuit breakers are connected to live wire of a device, so if current surges...

...fuse melts or circuit breaker trips...

...circuit breaks and appliance is isolated, preventing fires/shocks.

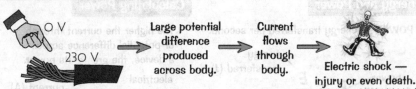

Electric Fields

Electric Fields Around A Point Charge

ELECTRIC FIELD — a region in which another charged object feels a force.

An electric field is created around any electrically charged object.

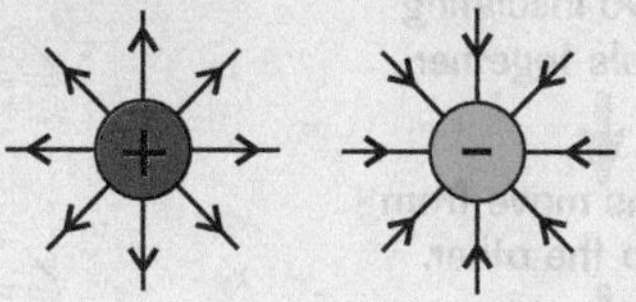

Strong electric fields ionise air particles, which can cause sparks.

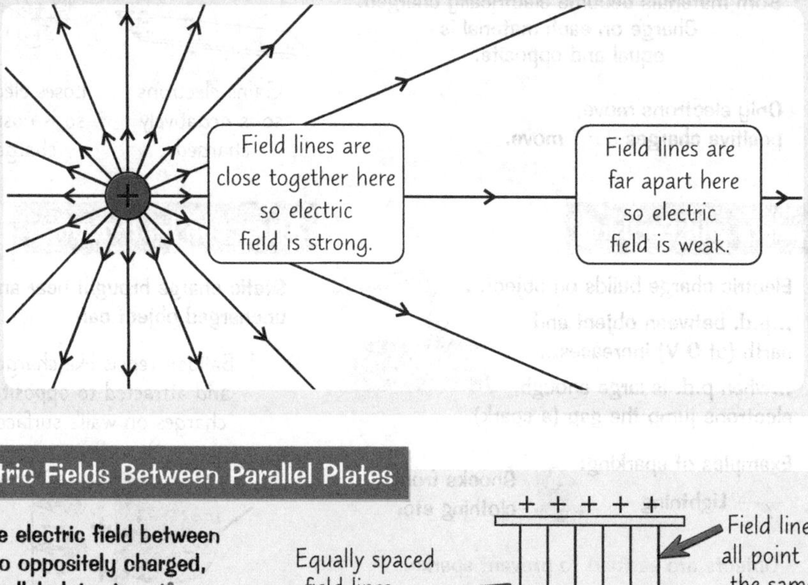
Field lines are close together here so electric field is strong.
Field lines are far apart here so electric field is weak.

Electric Fields Between Parallel Plates

The electric field between two oppositely charged, parallel plates is uniform.

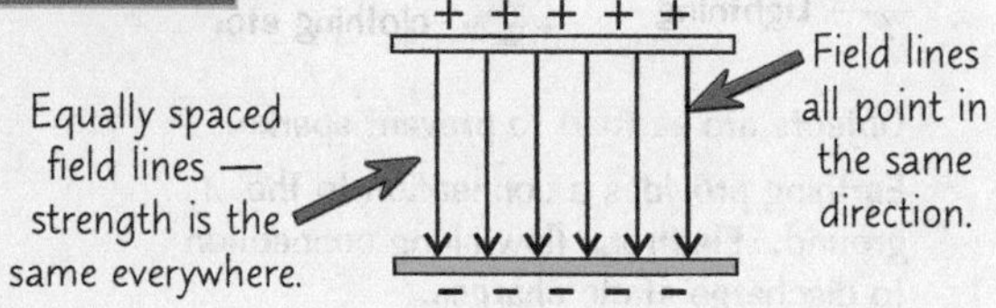
Equally spaced field lines — strength is the same everywhere.
Field lines all point in the same direction.

Attraction and Repulsion of Charges

When a charged object is placed in the electric field of another charged object, they both feel a force.

Unlike charges attract: **Like charges repel:**

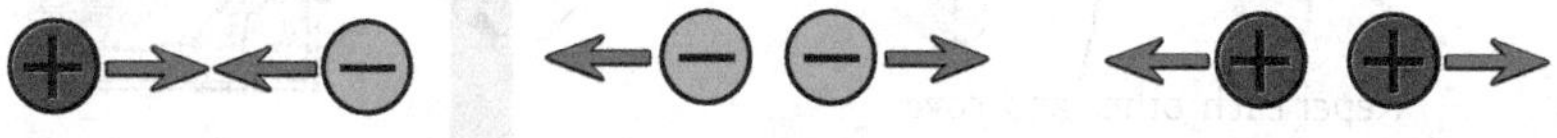

Static Electricity

Static Charging by Friction

Rub two insulating materials together.

↓

Electrons move from one to the other.

↓

Both materials become electrically charged. Charge on each material is equal and opposite.

Only electrons move, positive charges don't move.

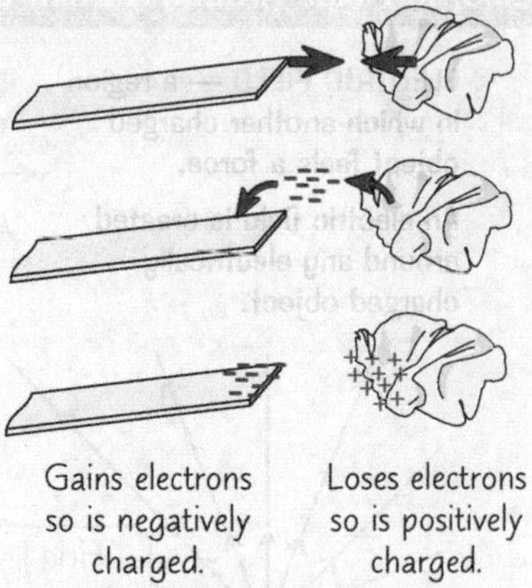
Gains electrons so is negatively charged.
Loses electrons so is positively charged.

Sparks and Earthing

Electric charge builds on object...

...p.d. between object and earth (at 0 V) increases...

...when p.d. is large enough, electrons jump the gap (a spark).

Examples of sparking:

 **Lightning**  **Shocks from clothing etc.**

Objects are earthed to prevent sparks. Earthing provides a connection to the ground. Electrons flow along connection to discharge static charges.

Attraction by Induction

Static charge brought near an uncharged object can induce charge.

Balloon repels like charges and attracted to opposite charges on wall's surface

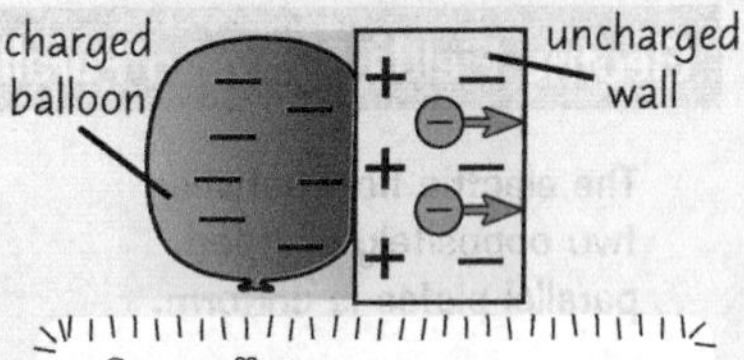
charged balloon
uncharged wall

Same effect causes paper scraps to 'jump' toward a charged comb.

Electrostatic Sprayers

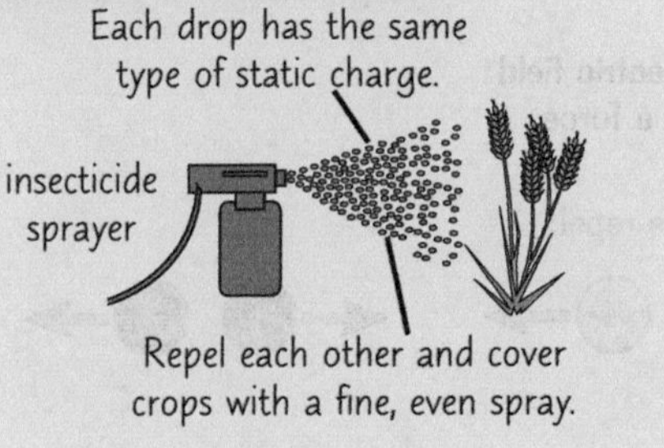
Each drop has the same type of static charge.
insecticide sprayer
Repel each other and cover crops with a fine, even spray.

Dangers

Static charge can build up while fuelling cars. A spark could ignite the fuel and cause an explosion.

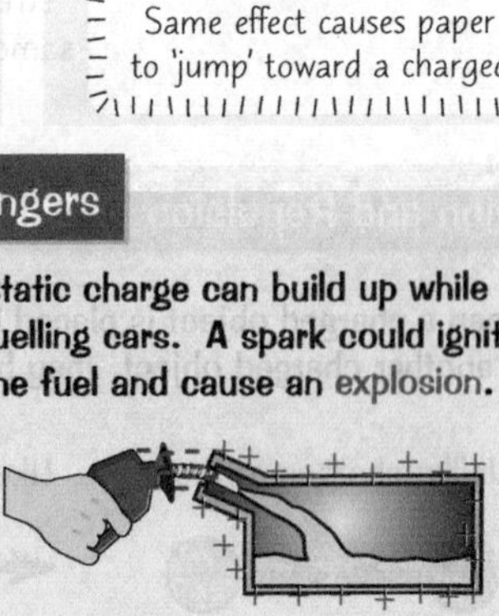

Fuel tanks are earthed to prevent this.

Magnets

Magnetic Fields

PERMANENT MAGNET — produces its own magnetic field.

Magnetic field is strongest at the poles.

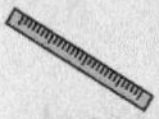

Magnetic field strength decreases with distance from magnet.

Field lines show direction force would act on a north pole, if placed at that point.

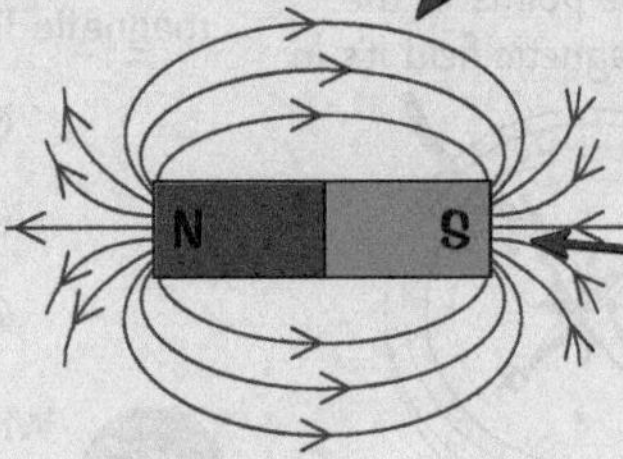

MAGNETIC FIELD — region where other magnets or magnetic materials experience a force.

Field is stronger where field lines are closer together.

Forces between magnets are due to their magnetic fields interacting.

Magnetic Repulsion

Like poles repel.

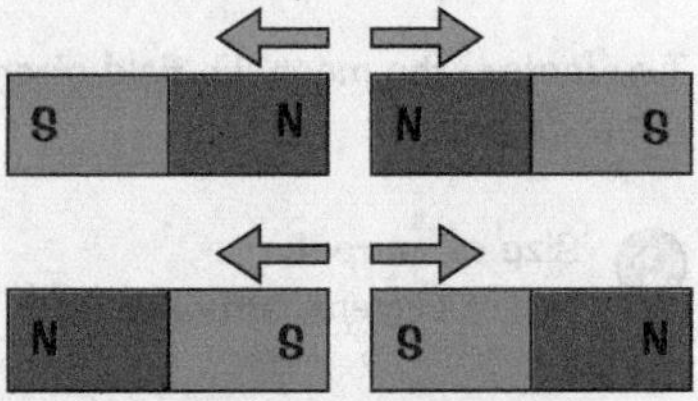

Magnetic Attraction

Unlike poles attract.

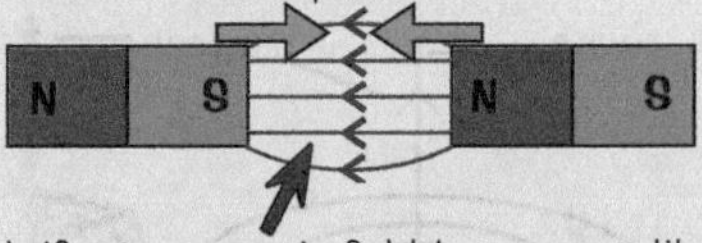

Uniform magnetic field between unlike poles — field lines equally spaced (strength same everywhere) and in same direction.

Induced Magnets and Magnetic Materials

INDUCED MAGNET — a magnetic material that only produces a magnetic field when it's in another magnetic field.

permanent magnet   induced magnet

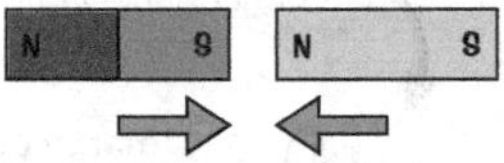

A permanent magnet and an induced magnet are always attracted to each other.

When the induced magnet is moved away from the permanent magnet, it quickly loses all (or most) of its magnetism.

Four magnetic materials:

1. **iron**
2. **steel**
3. **nickel**
4. **cobalt**

Uses of Magnets

Fridge doors

Separating recycling

Maglev trains

Cranes

Compasses and the Motor Effect

Compasses

Compass needle points in the direction of the magnetic field it's in.

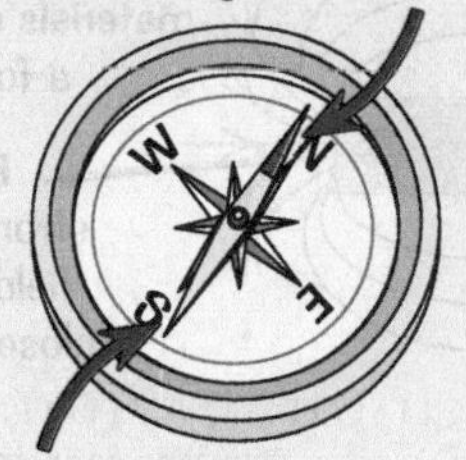

A compass needle is a small bar magnet.

Place a compass at different positions in a magnetic field to show its shape and direction.

When a compass isn't near a magnet, its needle points north. This is because Earth produces its own magnetic field (Earth's core is magnetic).

Current-Carrying Conductor

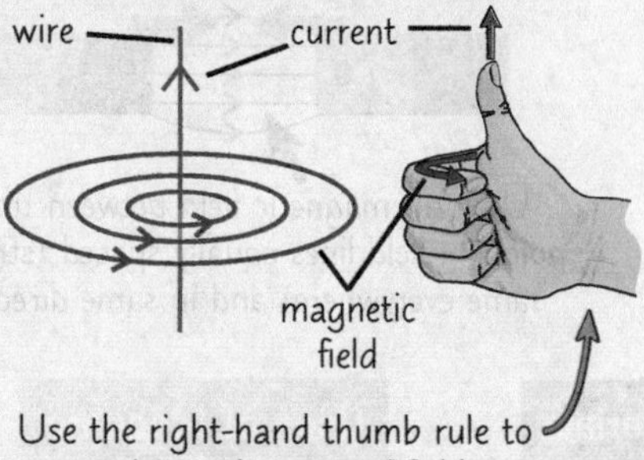

Use the right-hand thumb rule to work out direction of field.

Two factors the magnetic field strength depends on:

1. **Size of current.**
   Larger current, stronger field.
2. **Distance from the conductor.**
   Closer = stronger field.

Force on a Conductor

MOTOR EFFECT — when a magnet and a current-carrying conductor exert an equal and opposite force on each other.

Fleming's left-hand rule.

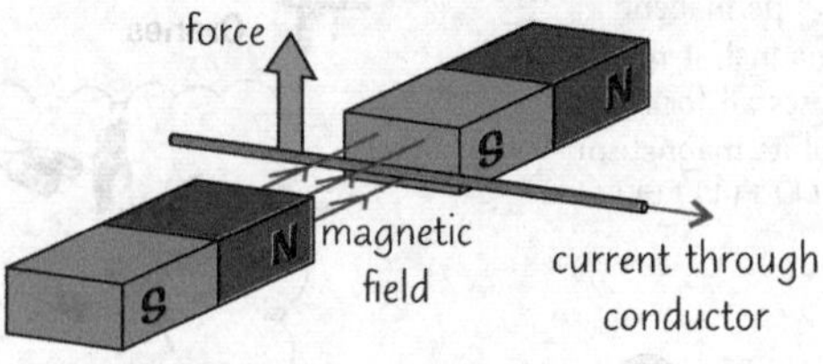

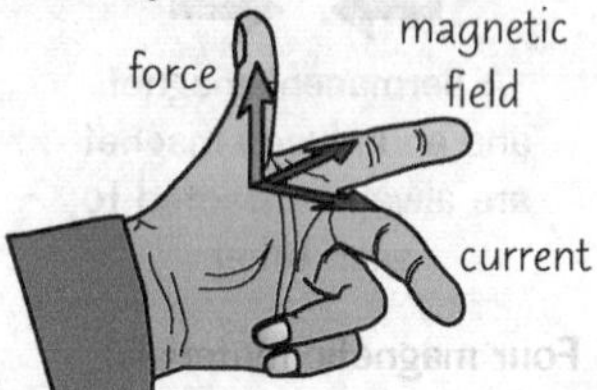

Motors, Solenoids and Induced P.d.

Electric Motors

Direct current is passed through wire.

↓

Each side of the coil experiences opposite forces.

↓

Coil rotates.

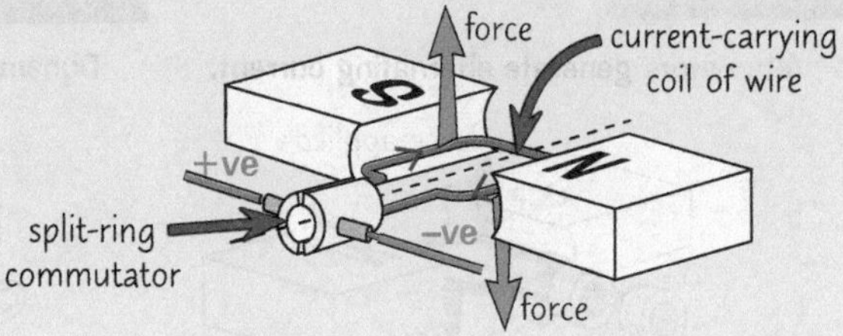
force
current-carrying coil of wire
+ve
split-ring commutator
–ve
force
S
N

Solenoids

SOLENOID — a long cylindrical coil of wire.

A solenoid is an example of an electromagnet.

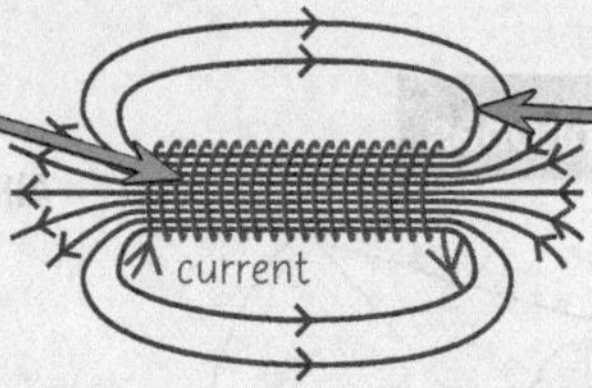
Inside solenoid, magnetic fields of each turn of wire add together to form strong and almost uniform field.
current
Outside solenoid, magnetic fields cancel to form weaker field, which is same shape as a bar magnet's field.

Electromagnetic Induction

ELECTROMAGNETIC INDUCTION — the induction of a p.d. (and current if there's a complete circuit) in a wire which is experiencing a change in magnetic field.

	1	2
Two ways to induce a potential difference...	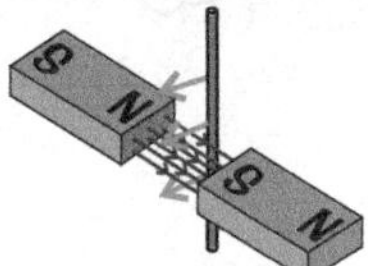 Move the wire.	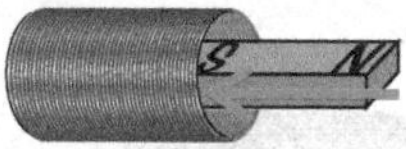 Move the magnet.
To swap the direction of the potential difference...	**Move the wire in the opposite direction. or Start with both magnets the other way round.**	**Move the magnet in the opposite direction. or Start with the magnet the other way round.**
To increase the size of the induced potential difference...	**Increase the speed of the movement. or Increase the magnetic field strength.**	

For a coil, can also increase turns per unit length.

An induced current generates its own magnetic field.
This magnetic field always acts against the change that made it.

Generators & Electromagnetic Devices

Alternators

Alternators generate alternating current.

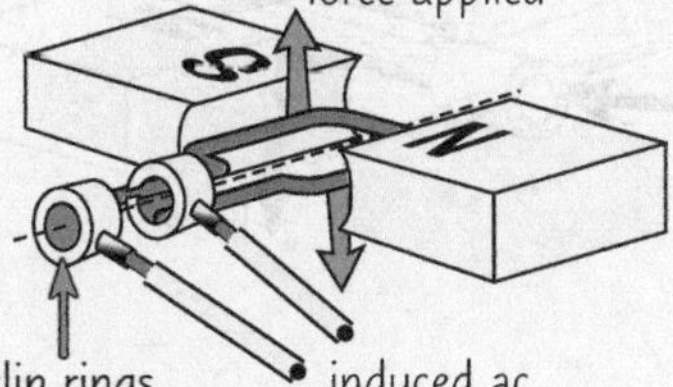

and brushes prevent contacts from swapping as it turns

Dynamos

Dynamos generate direct current.

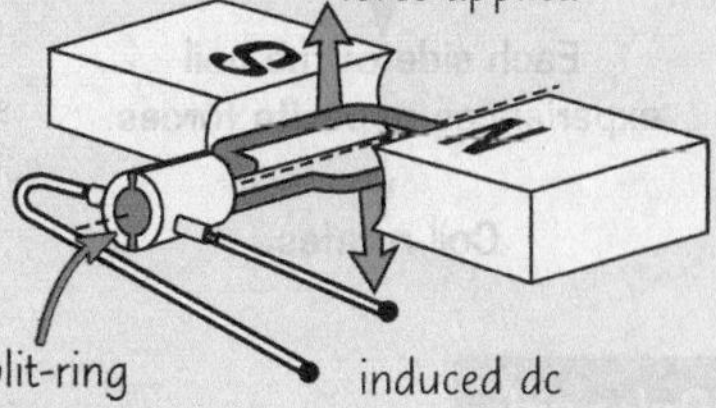

commutator swaps contacts each half turn

Loudspeakers and Headphones

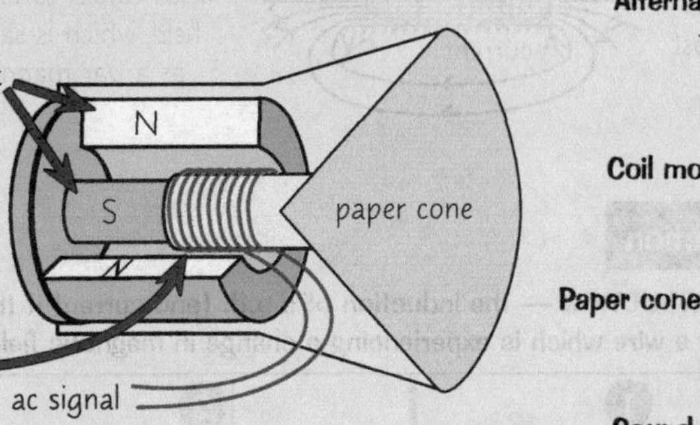

Alternating current is sent through coil.

↓

Coil moves back and forth.

↓

Paper cone moves back and forth.

↓

Sound waves are created.

Microphones

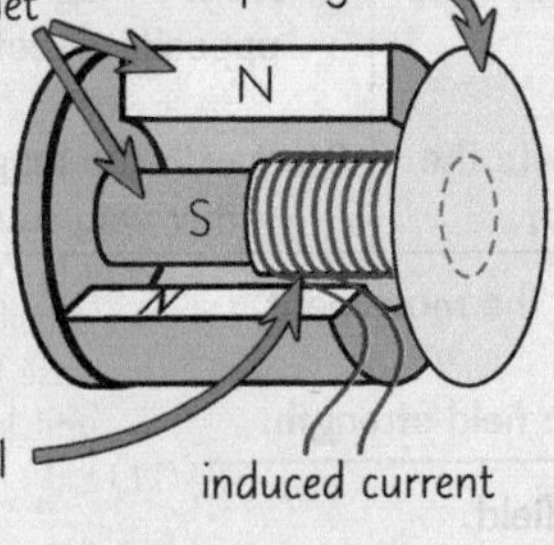

Sound waves hit diaphragm.

↓

Diaphragm moves back and forth.

↓

Coil of wire moves back and forth.

↓

Alternating current is generated.

Transformers and the National Grid

Transformers

Alternating current passed through primary coil. $\Rightarrow$ Changing magnetic field induced in iron core. $\Rightarrow$ Alternating current induced in secondary coil.

Step-up transformer
$V_P < V_s$

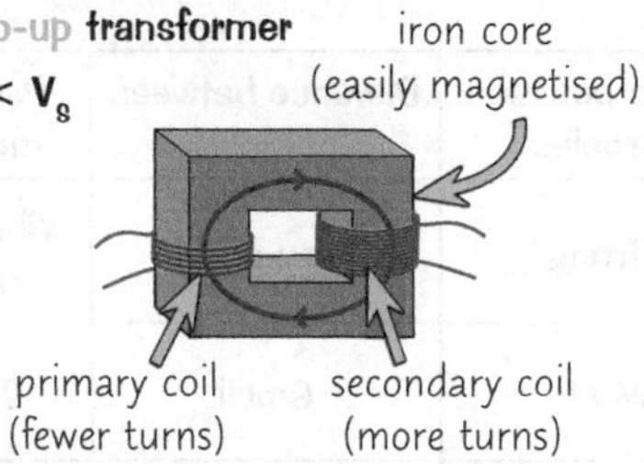

iron core (easily magnetised)

primary coil (fewer turns)   secondary coil (more turns)

Step-down transformer
$V_P > V_s$

magnetic field

primary coil (more turns)   secondary coil (fewer turns)

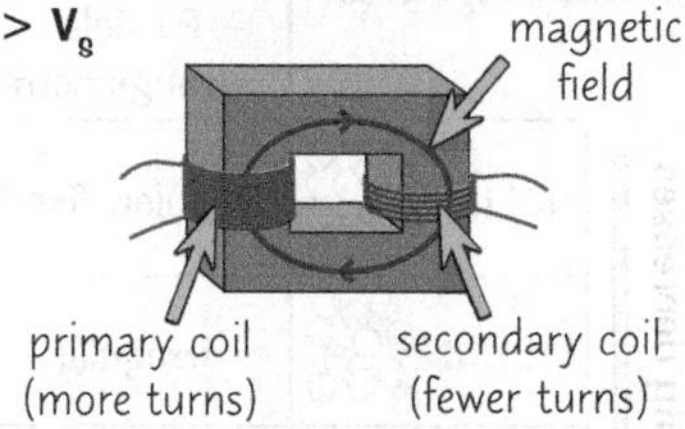

ratio between primary and secondary potential differences
= ratio between number of turns on primary and secondary coils

If transformer is 100% efficient: input power = output power.

Changing the number of turns on a coil changes the output p.d.

Power Stations

boiler

turbine   generator (huge magnet inside coil)

fuel injected

electricity sent to national grid

fuel burned to heat   ...which turns   ...which turns generator,
water to steam...   turbine...   producing a.c.

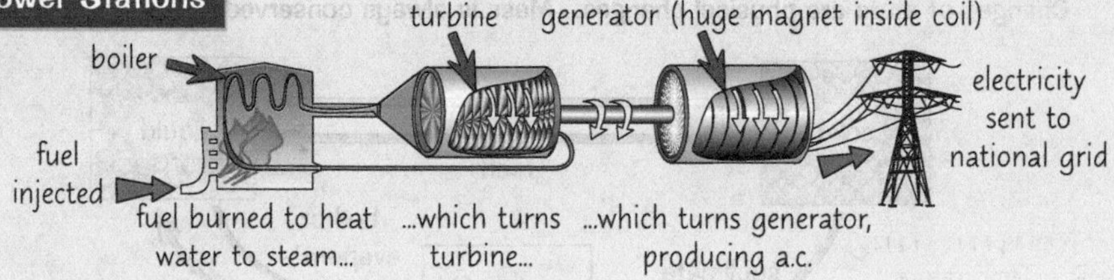

The National Grid

NATIONAL GRID — a system of cables and transformers that connect power stations to consumers.

Electrical power transferred at a high potential difference and a low current. This is more efficient as it reduces energy losses to thermal stores, as high currents would heat up wires.

power station

consumers

step-up transformer — increases potential difference to transmit huge amount of power efficiently

step-down transformer — decreases potential difference to bring it down to safe, usable levels

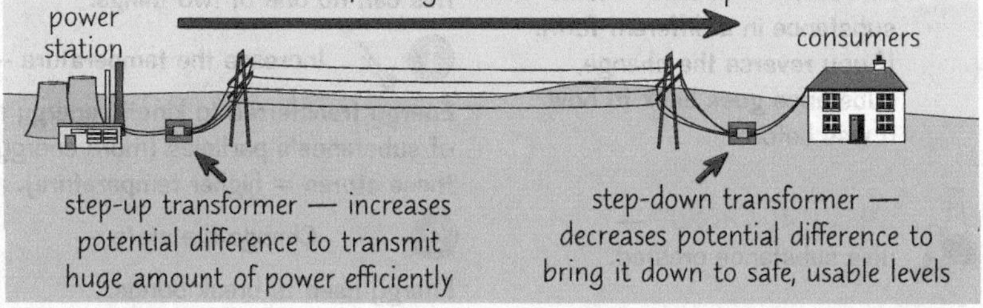

Density and The Particle Model

Density

DENSITY — mass per unit volume.

$$\rho = \frac{m}{V}$$

density (kg/m³), mass (kg), volume (m³)

States of Matter

Density decreases (solid → liquid → gas)

	Particle arrangement	Forces between particles	Distance between particles	Particle motion
SOLID	Regular, fixed	Strong	Very small	Vibration only
LIQUID	Irregular	Weak	Small	Slow
GAS	Irregular	Very weak	Large	Fast

Changes of State

Changes of state **are physical changes. Mass is always conserved.**

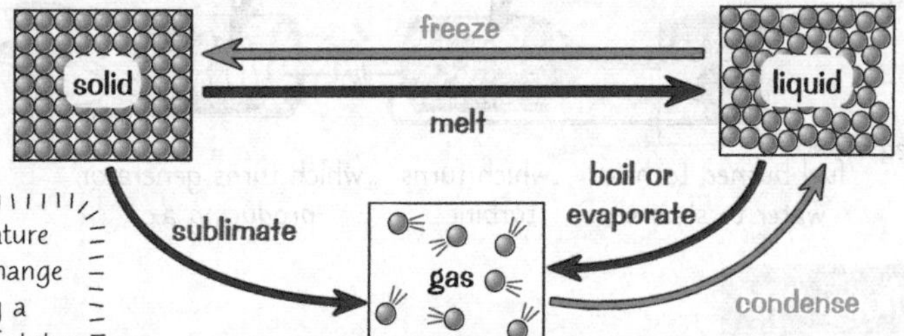

Temperature doesn't change during a change of state.

Physical and Chemical Changes

PHYSICAL CHANGE — **same substance in a different form. If you reverse the change, substance goes back to how it was before.**

CHEMICAL CHANGE — **new substance created.**

Heating

Heating transfers energy to a substance. This can do one of two things:

1. **Increase the temperature —**
Energy transferred to kinetic energy stores of substance's particles (more energy in these stores = higher temperature).

2. **Change the state —**
Energy used to break bonds.

Heating, Temperature and Pressure

Specific Heat Capacity and Specific Latent Heat

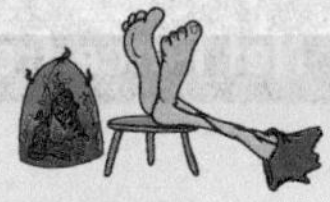

Specific feet capacity

SPECIFIC HEAT CAPACITY — the amount of energy needed to raise the temperature of 1 kg of a substance by 1 °C.

SPECIFIC LATENT HEAT — the amount of energy needed to change 1 kg of a substance from one state to another, without changing its temperature.

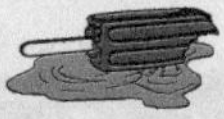

SPECIFIC LATENT HEAT OF FUSION — the specific latent heat of changing between a solid and a liquid.

SPECIFIC LATENT HEAT OF VAPORISATION — the specific latent heat of changing between a liquid and a gas.

Absolute Zero

Converting between kelvin and Celsius:

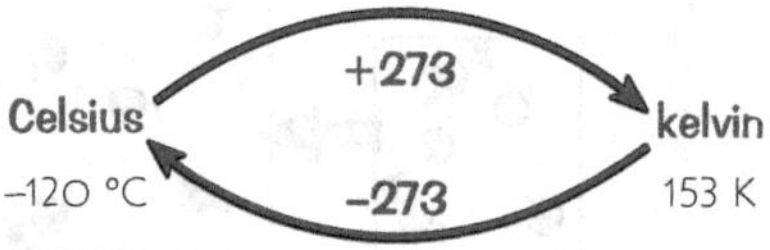

This is MINUS 273.

ABSOLUTE ZERO — 0 K, or −273 °C. The temperature at which particles have as little energy as possible in their kinetic energy stores — they're almost still.

Absolute zero is the coldest possible temperature.

Gas Pressure

Gas particles are constantly moving randomly.

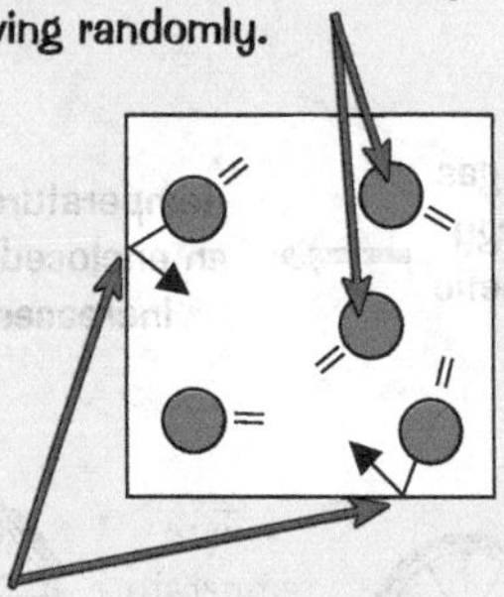

When particles collide with a surface...

... they exert a force, and so a pressure.

A Gas at Constant Volume

Temperature increases

↓

Particles get faster and collide with the container with more force and more often.

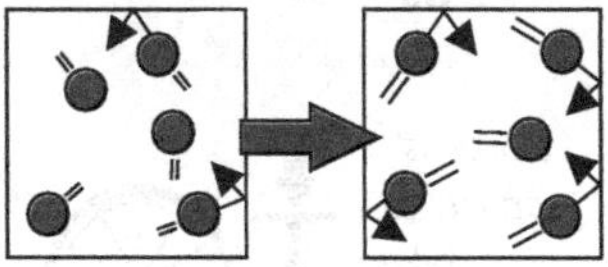

↓

Pressure increases

Pressure and Work on Gases

Net Force from Gas Pressure

All the collisions of the gas particles with a surface add to produce a net force on that surface.

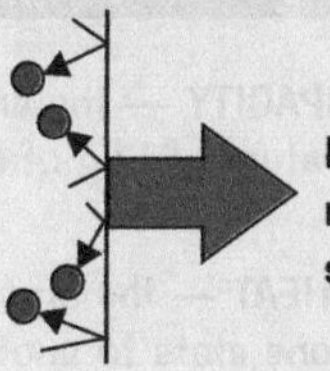

Net force acts at right angles to the surface.

Pressure Changes

For a gas inside a container that can change size (e.g. a balloon), pressure changes cause volume changes:

pressure outside > pressure inside → gas is compressed

pressure outside < pressure inside → gas expands

A Gas at Constant Temperature

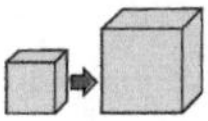

Volume increases

↓

Particles spread out and collide with the container less often.

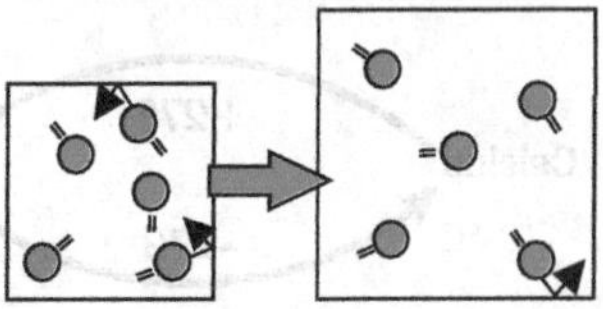

↓

Pressure decreases

Doing Work on Gases

Force is applied to gas. Work is done as energy is transferred. → Doing work on the gas increases the energy in gas particles' kinetic energy stores. → Temperature of an enclosed gas increases.

Force is applied to air in bike pump and tyre.

Energy in air particles' kinetic energy stores increases in tyre.

Tyre temperature increases.

Elasticity

Changing Shape

More than one force has to act on a stationary object to change its shape.

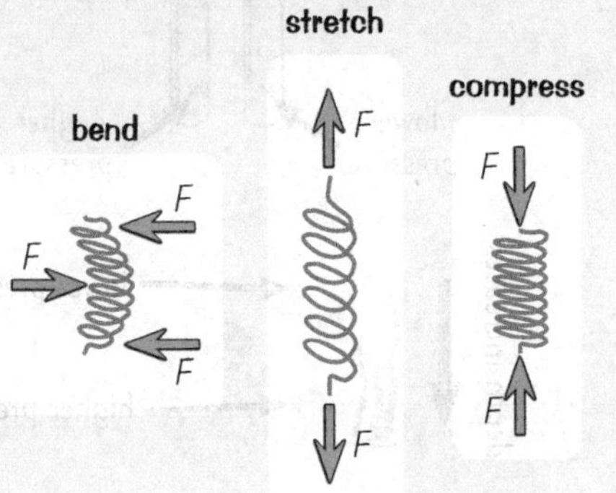
stretch
compress
bend
F
F
F
F
F
F
F

Two Types of Distortion

1. **ELASTIC — object goes back to its original shape and length after forces have been removed.**

Elastic objects can be elastically distorted, e.g. a spring.

2. **INELASTIC — object doesn't go back to its original shape and length after forces have been removed.**

Force-Extension Relationship for an Elastic Object

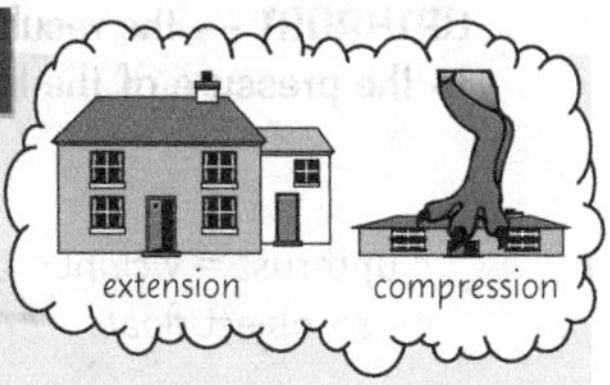
extension
compression

$$F = kx$$

- force (N) — F
- spring constant (N/m) — k
- extension or compression (m) — x

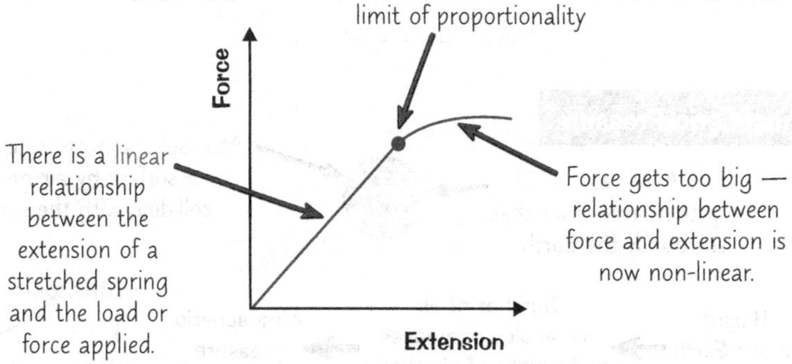
limit of proportionality
Force
Extension
There is a linear relationship between the extension of a stretched spring and the load or force applied.
Force gets too big — relationship between force and extension is now non-linear.

Fluid Pressure and Upthrust

Pressure

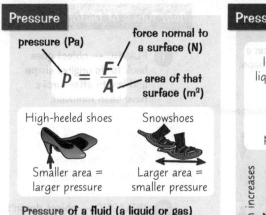

$$P = \frac{F}{A}$$

pressure (Pa) — P

force normal to a surface (N) — F

area of that surface (m²) — A

High-heeled shoes

Smaller area = larger pressure

Snowshoes

Larger area = smaller pressure

Pressure of a fluid (a liquid or gas) means a force is exerted normal to any surface in contact with the fluid.

Pressure Differences in a Fluid

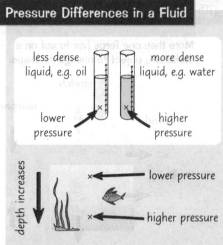

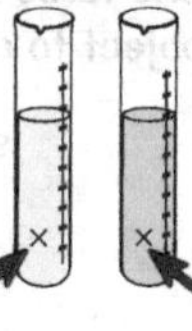
less dense liquid, e.g. oil
more dense liquid, e.g. water
lower pressure
higher pressure

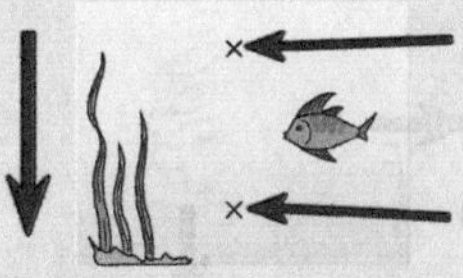
depth increases
lower pressure
higher pressure

Upthrust

UPTHRUST — the resultant force acting upwards on an object submerged in liquid, due to the pressure of the liquid being greater at the bottom of the object than at the top.

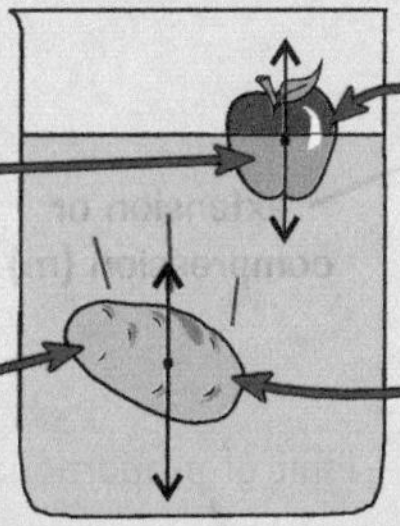
upthrust = weight so object floats
object is less dense than liquid
upthrust less than weight so object sinks
object is denser than liquid

Upthrust is equal to weight of liquid that has been displaced by object.

Atmospheric Pressure

THE ATMOSPHERE — a thin layer of air that surrounds the Earth.

Atmospheric pressure is created on a surface by air molecules colliding with the surface.

Height above Earth increases. → **Number of air molecules decreases and weight of air above a surface decreases.** → **Atmospheric pressure decreases.**

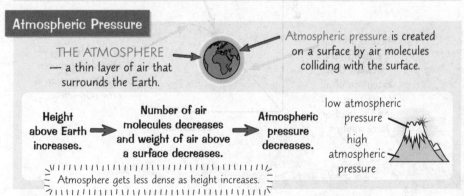

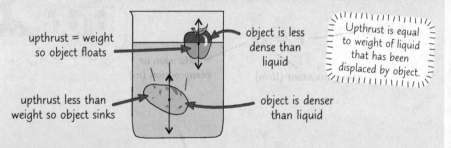

low atmospheric pressure
high atmospheric pressure

Atmosphere gets less dense as height increases.

Core Practicals 1

Two Experiments that Test $F = ma$

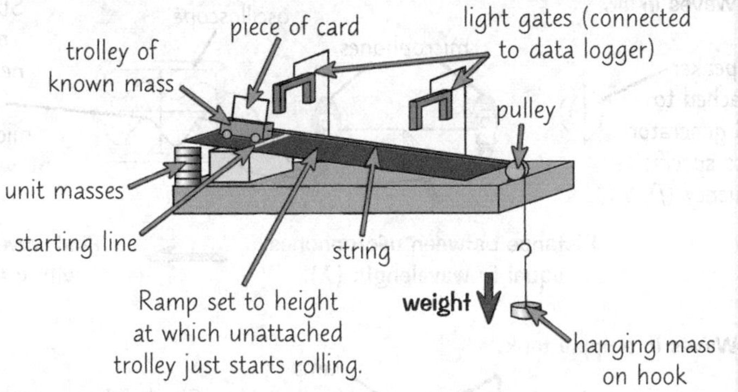
piece of card
light gates (connected
to data logger)
trolley of
known mass
pulley
unit masses
starting line
string
Ramp set to height
at which unattached
trolley just starts rolling.
weight
hanging mass
on hook

1 Investigate effect of mass

- **Add unit mass to trolley.**
- **Release trolley from starting line.**
  Light gates record trolley's acceleration.
- **Add another mass to trolley and repeat until all masses added.**

Each light gate measures speed and time when trolley passes through. Acceleration is found from change in speed ÷ time taken.

Independent Variable	Dependent Variable	Control Variable
mass	acceleration	force (weight)

Increasing mass decreases acceleration.

2 Investigate effect of force

- **Start with all unit masses on trolley.**
- **Release trolley from starting line.**
  Light gates record trolley's acceleration.
- **Move a mass from trolley to hook and repeat measurement.**
- **Keep going until all masses moved.**

Safety Tip #314 — be careful with hooks...

Independent Variable	Dependent Variable	Control Variable
force (weight)	acceleration	mass

Increasing force applied increases acceleration.

Core Practicals 2

Measuring Properties of Three Different Waves

1 Waves in air.

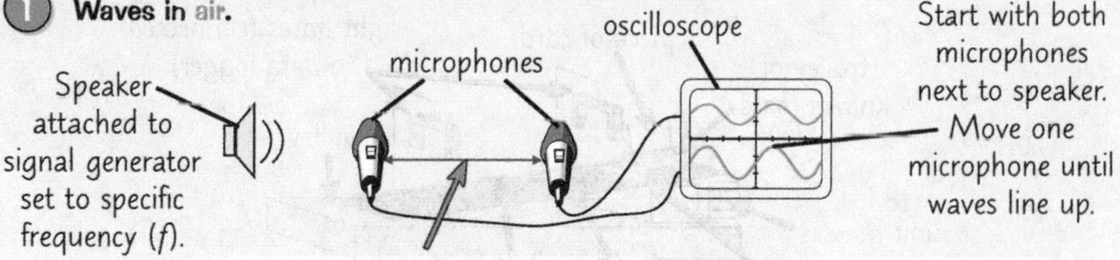
oscilloscope
microphones
Speaker attached to signal generator set to specific frequency (f).
Start with both microphones next to speaker. Move one microphone until waves line up.

Distance between microphones equal to wavelength (λ). → **Find wave speed with $v = f\lambda$.**

2 Waves in a ripple tank.

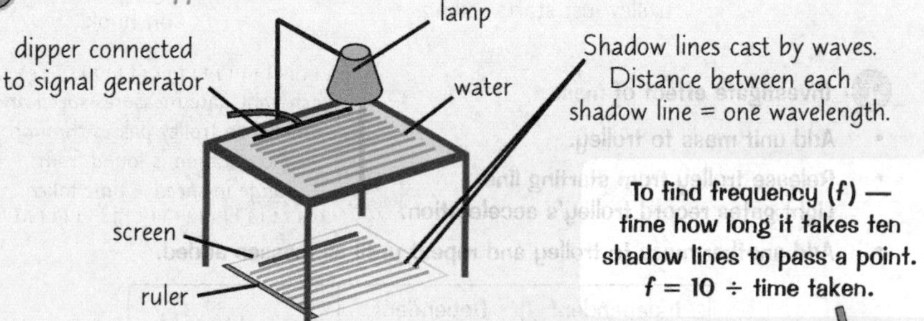
lamp
dipper connected to signal generator
water
Shadow lines cast by waves. Distance between each shadow line = one wavelength.
screen
ruler

To find frequency (f) — time how long it takes ten shadow lines to pass a point. $f = 10 \div$ time taken.

To find average wavelength (λ) — measure distance between shadow lines that are ten wavelengths apart and divide by ten.

If you're struggling to measure this precisely, take a photo of screen and ruler.

→ **Find wave speed with $v = f\lambda$.**

3 Waves in a solid.

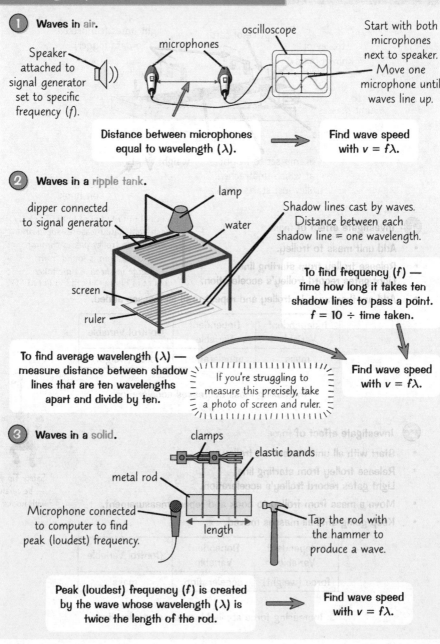

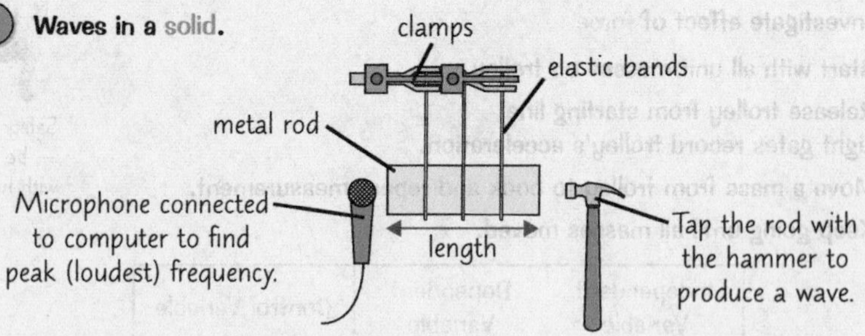
clamps
elastic bands
metal rod
Microphone connected to computer to find peak (loudest) frequency.
length
Tap the rod with the hammer to produce a wave.

Peak (loudest) frequency (f) is created by the wave whose wavelength (λ) is twice the length of the rod. → **Find wave speed with $v = f\lambda$.**

Core Practicals 3

Four Steps to Investigate Refraction

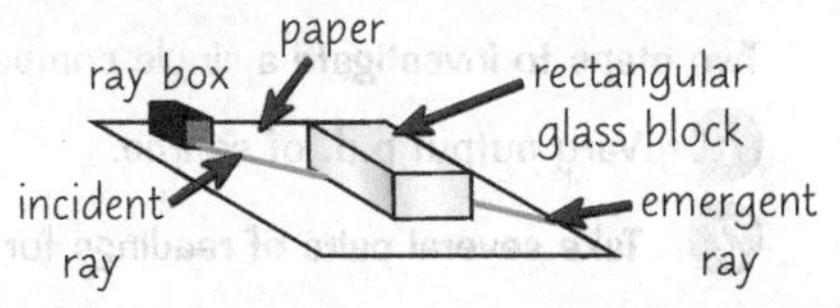

1. Trace around block, then trace incident ray and emergent ray.

2. Remove block and join incident ray and emergent ray with straight line (refracted ray).

3. Draw normal where incident ray enters block and measure angle of incidence, *I*, and angle of refraction, *R*.

Incident Ray: he's here to help.

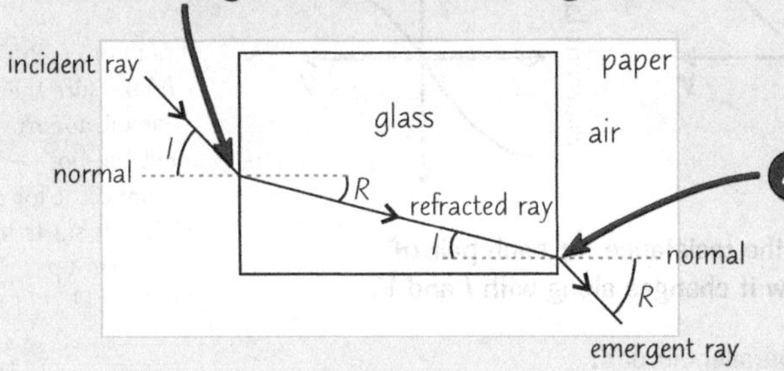

4. Do the same where ray emerges from block.

When the ray enters the block I > R and when it leaves R > I. This means:

Ray bends towards normal going from air to glass — light is slower in glass than air.
Ray bends away from normal going from glass to air — light is faster in air than glass.

Investigating Emission of Radiation

Boil water and fill each test tube with same volume.

Measure temperature of water at regular intervals. Temperature drops quicker if surface a better emitter.

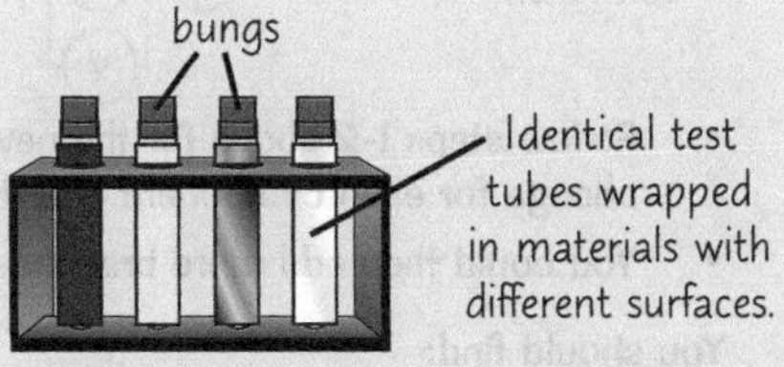

- A black surface is a better emitter than a white one.
- A matte surface is a better emitter than a shiny one.

Independent Variable	surface
Dependent Variable	rate of decrease of water temperature
Control Variables	e.g. volume of water, shape of test tube

Core Practicals 4

Investigating Components and Circuits

Two steps to investigate a single component:

1. **Vary output p.d. of source.**
2. **Take several pairs of readings for I and V.**

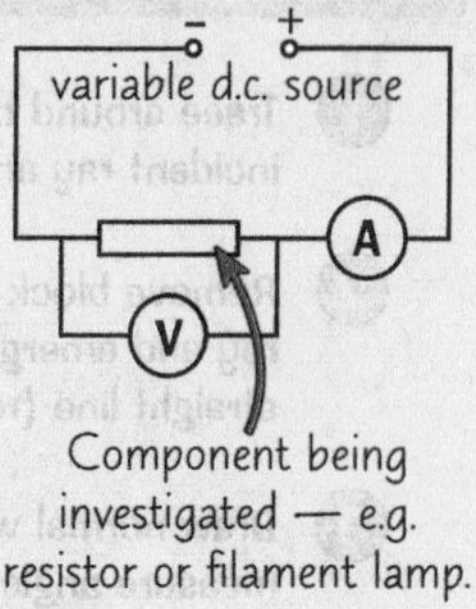

Plot values on I-V graph to show relationship between p.d. and current:

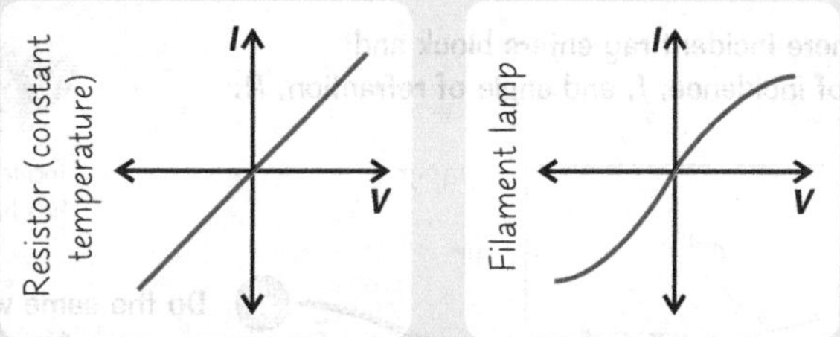

Use $V = IR$ to work out the resistance for each pair of measurements to see how it changes along with I and V.

Make sure the circuit doesn't get too hot — disconnect it for a while if it starts to warm up.

Investigating series and parallel circuits:

- **Using the circuit above, connect a second identical component either...**
  ...in parallel... **...or in series:**

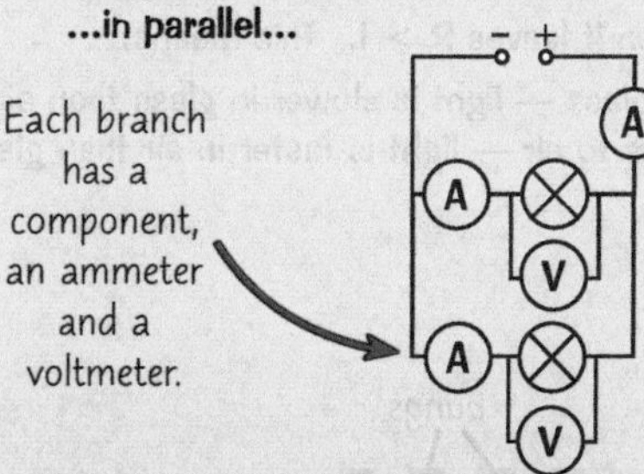

Each branch has a component, an ammeter and a voltmeter.
A
A
V
A
V

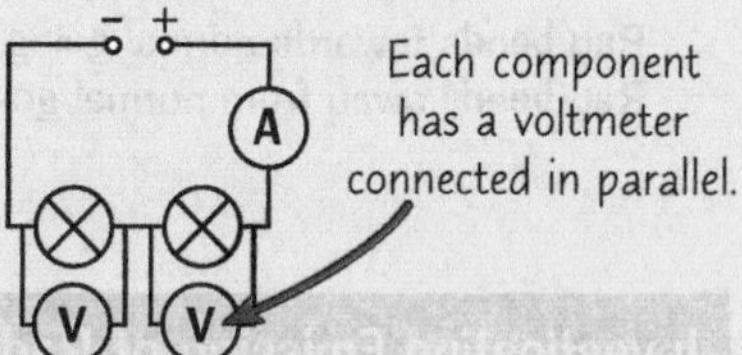

Each component has a voltmeter connected in parallel.
A
V
V

- **Follow steps 1-2 above for the new circuit — see how I and V change for each component and the circuit as a whole.**
- **You could then add more branches (in parallel) or more components (in series).**

You should find:

	Series	Parallel
Increase source p.d.	Total current through circuit also increases.	
P.d. across each component	Source p.d. shared between components.	Same as source p.d.
Total current through circuit	Same everywhere, decreases as components added.	Equals sum of current in branches, increases as components added.

Core Practicals 5

Determining Density of Solids and Liquids

To measure density of a solid or liquid, find its mass and volume, then use: → $\text{density (kg/m}^3\text{)} = \dfrac{\text{mass (kg)}}{\text{volume (m}^3\text{)}}$

Regular solid

Use balance to find mass. →

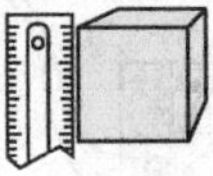

Measure object. Calculate volume using relevant formula for shape.

Irregular solid

mass of object = m_1

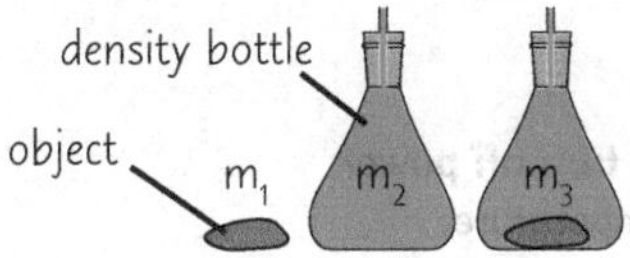

To find volume:

mass of displaced water = $m_1 + m_2 - m_3$

volume of displaced water = mass of displaced water ÷ density of water (known)

volume of object = volume of displaced water

Liquid

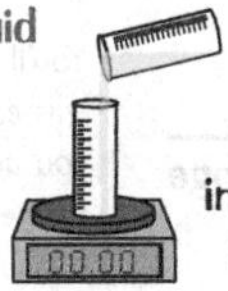

Pour 10 ml of liquid into measuring cylinder on balance set to 0. →

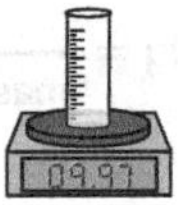

Record mass shown on balance and total volume shown on cylinder.

Investigating Springs

Four steps to find the relationship between force and extension:

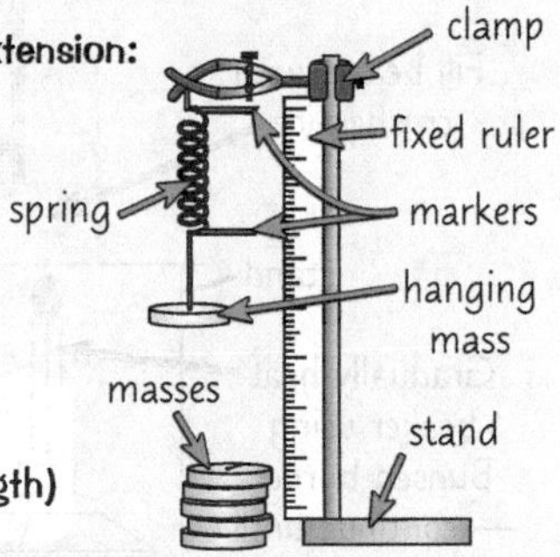

1. Measure natural length of spring with ruler.
2. Add mass to spring (causing it to extend).
3. Calculate force and extension:

Force = weight of masses = mg

(m is total mass on spring, g is gravitational field strength)

Extension = new length – natural length

Independent Variable	force applied to spring
Dependent Variable	extension

4. Add another mass and repeat readings. Plot a graph when you have at least 6 pairs of readings.

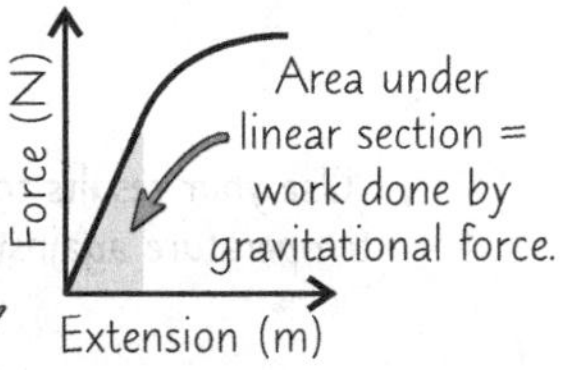

Core Practicals 6

Four Steps to Find the Specific Heat Capacity of Water

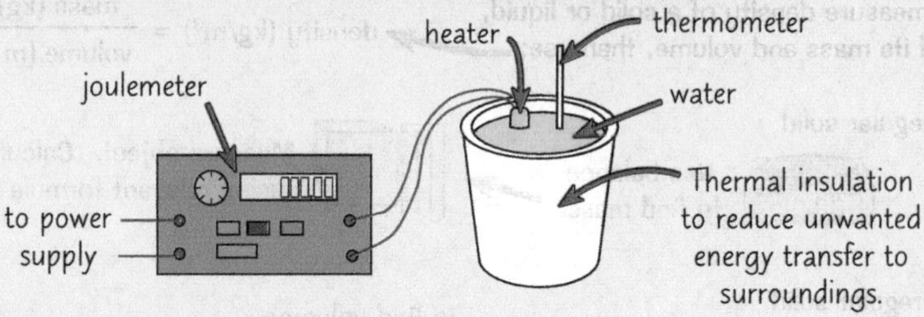

1. **Fill the container with a known mass of water.**
2. **Measure temperature and turn on power.**
3. **When temperature has increased e.g. 10 °C, turn off power. Record energy from joulemeter and final temperature.**
4. **Use your measurements to calculate specific heat capacity:**

$$\text{Specific heat capacity} = \frac{\text{energy supplied}}{\text{mass of water} \times \text{temperature change}}$$

You'll be given this equation — you don't have to memorise it.

Investigating Melting Ice

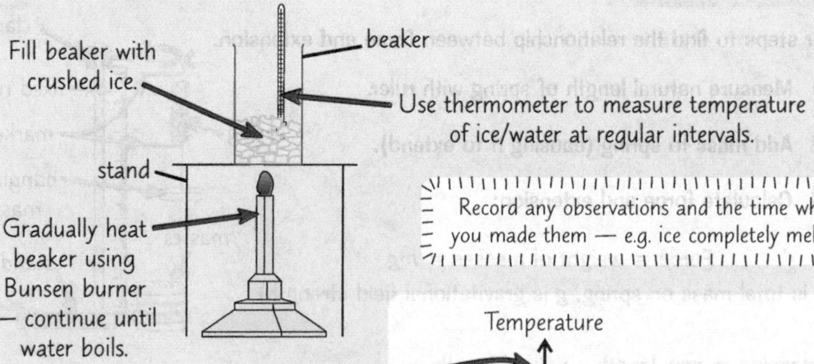

Record any observations and the time when you made them — e.g. ice completely melted.

Use your results to plot temperature against time.

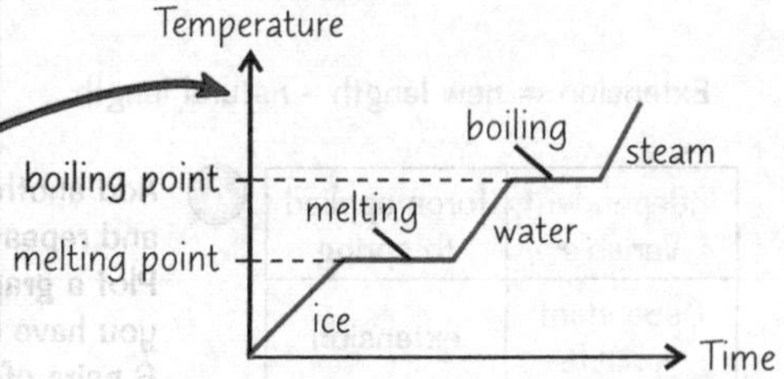

Apparatus and Techniques

Measuring Length

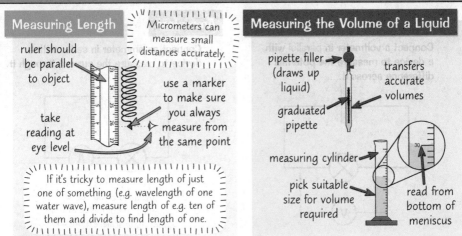

Micrometers can measure small distances accurately.

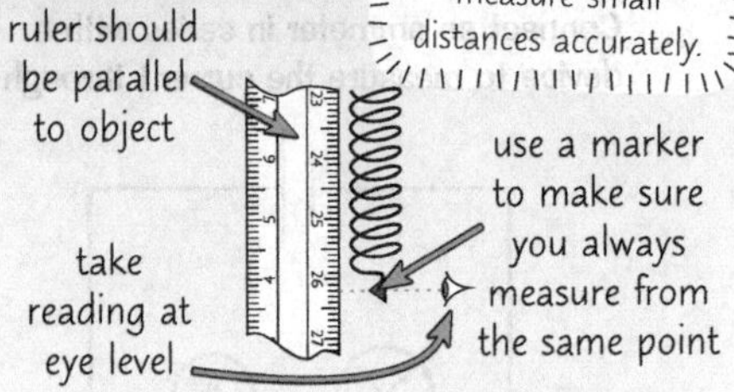
ruler should be parallel to object
take reading at eye level
use a marker to make sure you always measure from the same point

If it's tricky to measure length of just one of something (e.g. wavelength of one water wave), measure length of e.g. ten of them and divide to find length of one.

Measuring the Volume of a Liquid

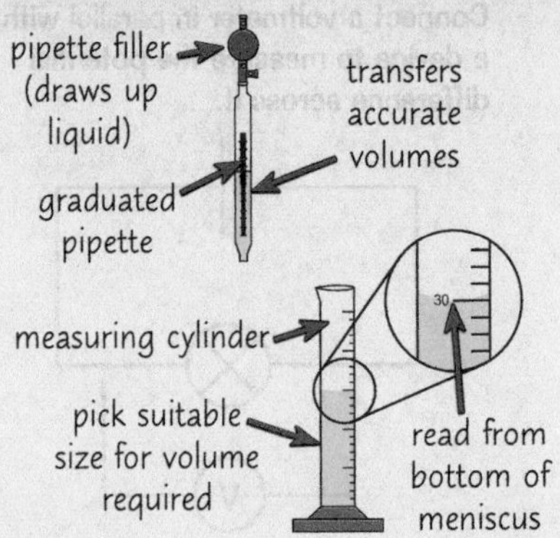
pipette filler (draws up liquid)
transfers accurate volumes
graduated pipette
measuring cylinder
30
pick suitable size for volume required
read from bottom of meniscus

Measuring Angles

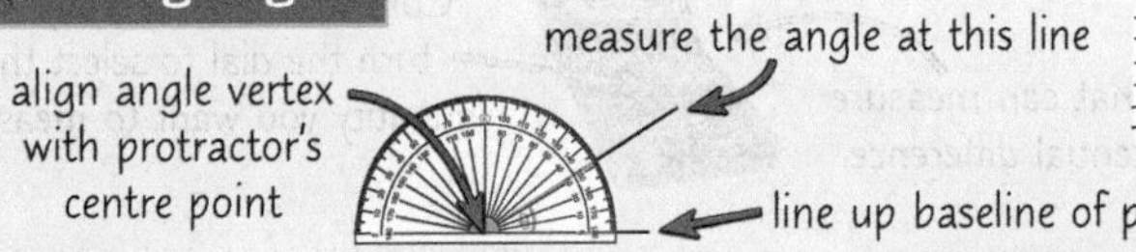
measure the angle at this line
align angle vertex with protractor's centre point
line up baseline of protractor with one angle line

Draw angles with a sharp pencil to reduce errors.

Safety

If using lasers, don't look directly into them.

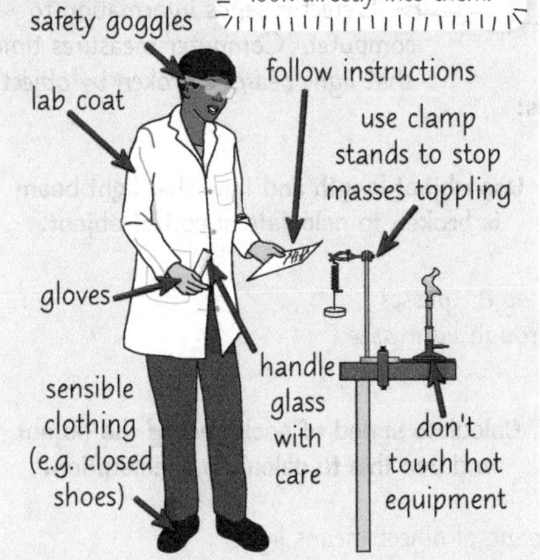
safety goggles
lab coat
follow instructions
use clamp stands to stop masses toppling
gloves
handle glass with care
sensible clothing (e.g. closed shoes)
don't touch hot equipment

Use low voltage and current when working with electronics to prevent overheating.

Measuring Temperature

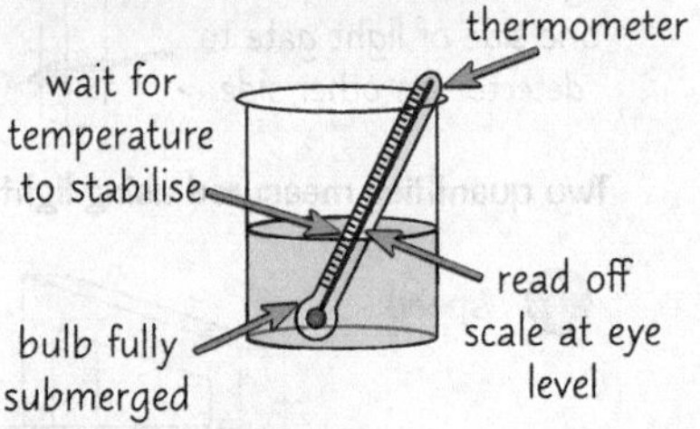
thermometer
wait for temperature to stabilise
read off scale at eye level
bulb fully submerged

Measuring Mass

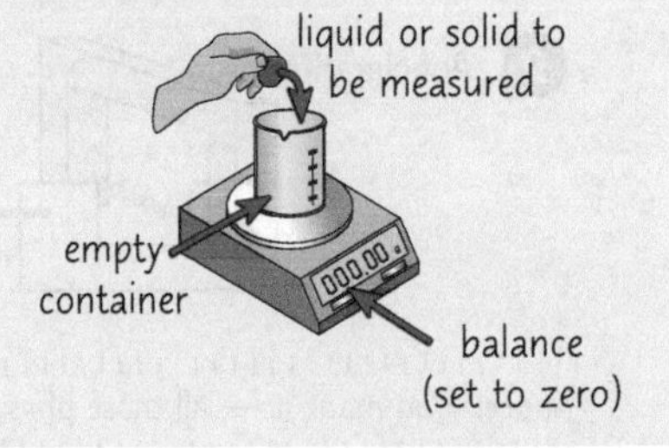
liquid or solid to be measured
empty container
000.00
balance (set to zero)

Working with Electronics

Voltmeters

Connect a voltmeter in parallel with a device to measure the potential difference across it.

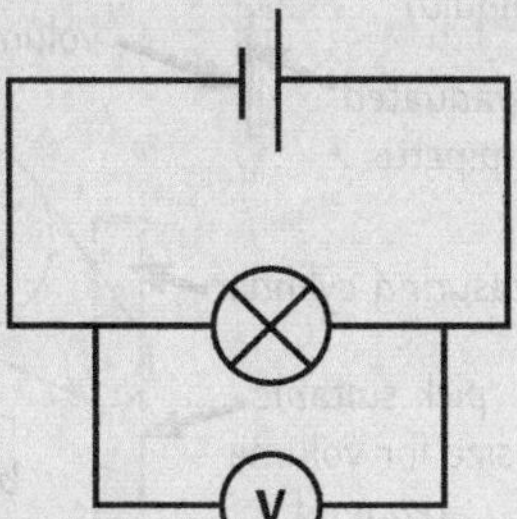
V

Ammeters

Connect an ammeter in series with a device to measure the current through it.

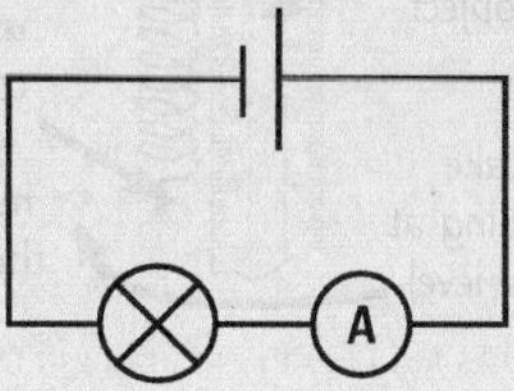
A

Make sure you use an ammeter or voltmeter with an appropriate scale, e.g. mA, mV.

Multimeters

Multimeters are devices that can measure current, resistance or potential difference.

Connect them correctly and turn the dial to select the quantity you want to measure.

Light Gates

Time can also be measured with a stopwatch.

Light beam is shone from one side of light gate to detector on other side.

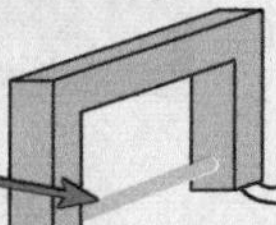

Detector sends information to computer. Computer measures time that light beam is broken by object.

Two quantities measured using light gates:

1. **Speed**

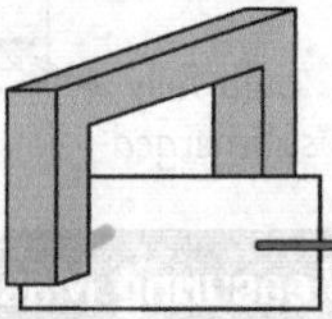
object passes through light gate

Use object length and time that light beam is broken to calculate speed of object.

2. **Acceleration**

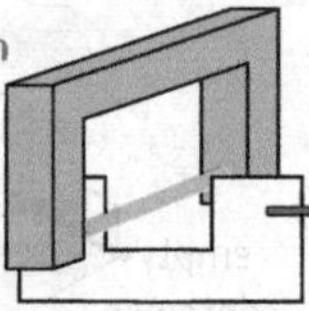
shape of object means light beam is interrupted twice

Calculate speed of each part of the object and use this to calculate acceleration.

Yippee! You made it — all those physics facts and you got through them all. Bravo my friend.